W9-AQN-918

The Mystery of Physical Life

The Mystery of Physical Life

E. GRANT WATSON

with a Preface by
Owen Barfield

Abelard - Schuman
LONDON NEW YORK TORONTO

Library of Congress Catalogue Card Number 64—13924

First published 1964

LONDON
Abelard-Schuman
Limited
8 King Street WC2

NEW YORK
Abelard-Schuman
Limited
6 West 57 Street

TORONTO
Abelard-Schuman
Canada Limited
896 Queen Street West

CONTENTS

APPENDICES

ACKNOWLEDGEMENTS

Mrs Ida Bedford for her careful typing and retyping of my script.

Mrs Mary Adams, for permission to use extracts from her husband's published works to furnish a long note in the Appendix on Negative Space.

To the Editor of *The British Homoeopathic Journal* for permission to reprint extracts from "Potentisation and the peripheral forces of nature" (*The British Homoeopathic Journal*, Vol. 50 No. 4, October 1961) and for the loan of the blocks for the original illustrations to this article.

Messrs Putnam & Co. Ltd., for permission to reprint an extract from *Out of Africa*, by Karen Blixen.

PREFACE

Future historians will, I suspect, lay emphasis on two movements of thought which characterise the present age, one of them very much in the public eye and the other very much out of it.

The first is a persistent attempt to explore the unconscious mind; the second, a growing doubt concerning the true relation between man and nature. The former field of enquiry still has the charm of novelty. With the latter it is not so much the topic itself that is novel, but rather a waxing dissatisfaction with what for our immediate forbears was classical and established theory. In the science of physics the "classical" theory has had to be abandoned altogether and there is a growing suspicion in many quarters that in other realms too, such as biology, it may have to be abandoned before long. Anyone who keeps his eyes and ears open knows quite well that the classical theory of evolution from simple to complex, from the lifeless to the living, from mindlessness to mind, is by no means the *res judicata* which the BBC, for instance, would have us believe.

Indeed on this issue there have always been dissenting judgments, many of them delivered by weighty authorities, though the *Zeitgeist* has seen to it that they remained largely unheard. Such an authority was Adam Sedgwick, Cambridge Professor of Zoology, who in the earlier years of this century was exhorting his pupils to concentrate on the *facts* rather than the theories – and privately pointing out to them that, if they did so, they would find whole groups of facts which contradicted any theory of evolution so far advanced. He himself, he told them, believed that archetypal forms of plants and animals were "precipitated". One of those pupils was E. L. Grant Watson.

Is there any connection between these two streams of thought, these two contemporary preoccupations, to which I have drawn attention? The answer to this question is the heart of this book. Cogently the author argues that the unconscious, which psychology seeks to explore, cannot be divorced from what is elsewhere called "instinct"; that, in the higher orders of being, the line between conscious purpose and conscious thought on the one hand and instinct on the other is difficult or impossible to draw, while in the lower forms of life the line between instinct on the one hand and physiological function on the other is equally indeterminate. And, if physiological function in the lower orders is, as he maintains, virtually one with their form, their tissue and even their environment, may it not be that the *terra incognita* of psychology is related to, is in fact identical with, an archetypal realm from which the forms of nature herself are "precipitated" as evolution proceeds?

Yet it is not primarily as a philosophical enquirer that Mr Grant Watson takes us by the hand and leads us gently into "that region where conscious thought mingles with the unconscious springs of being." It is as an observer. A detached observer? Yes, and no. For he has the impartiality and humour of detachment without its coldness. Readers of *Enigmas of Natural History, The Leaves Return* and *Profitable Wonders* and others of his books do not need me to tell them of the peculiar quality of genetic sympathy, of participation amounting almost to symbiosis, with which the author has throughout his life been looking upon and penetrating the changing face and creatures of nature, or how often that quality enters as a sort of quiet and loving wisdom into the language of his descriptions. In such descriptions this book, too, abounds.

Love is of man, but wisdom is of nature, and there are times when it almost seems that the author's secret – as perhaps it will one day be the secret of a reformed scientific method – is to stand aside and let the wisdom of nature herself speak through him. Well read he obviously is and at home in both of the two cultures; yet it is not often from the rostrum or the dais that the persuasive word proceeds. More often it comes from inside the bell of the jelly-fish, where imagination has lurked with the little fish who enjoy the protection of the medusan stinging-cells from which they are themselves miraculously immune; or out of the tiny inverted cone, compounded of her own excretions, and hung up by the female sand-wasp in the little domed house of sand spicules that she began to build for the cone, and for the egg it is to receive, so long before her time was near. No wonder that the tentative conclusions which from time to time are drawn seem less like the last step of a syllogism than an emanation from the object or the process itself.

But there is also the other movement of the author's thought – the exploration of the unconscious mind. If his answer to the crucial question is correct, it follows that this is nothing less than an approach by an opposite route towards the *same* goal, the *same terra incognita*. And here too we shall find him specially well equipped for the journey. He has long been a serious student of modern psychology and of late years has himself practised with success in psychiatry. It would have been strange if his studies had not led him towards his famous contemporary, whose own explorations of the unconscious have ended in making the word "archetype" almost a household word. Study led to correspondence and correspondence culminated in personal acquaintance with the already venerable C. G. Jung, who read in manuscript and commented on some of the chapters which follow. Quotations from that correspondence, in text and footnote, now form an agreeable obbligato accompaniment to their main tenor.

What is remarkable here however is the way in which the two approaches are combined and interwoven with one another, often in the same paragraph and sometimes even in the same sentence. Or perhaps "interwoven" is not the best word to choose, since the two are, as I have said, directionally opposite, and such opposites do not so much combine as reciprocate. A better metaphor might be the alternating current from the generator which produces the steady electric light in the home. Certainly their resultant energy has carried Mr Grant Watson – as his chapter-titles indicate – far beyond the province ordinarily assigned to either psychology, or biology, and has enabled him to shed, in passing, an unexpectedly clear light even on such abstract and apparently fruitless questions as: What is chance? or Is there such a thing as "negative space"?

However it may best be depicted, it is undoubtedly this duality of approach, founded on a deeply double underlying experience, which is above all else the distinguishing feature of the work before us. If I have been able to give the reader an advance hint of that distinction, I have done all that I can hope to do; and in any case it is high time the author began to speak for himself. I will only add my own profound conviction that there are few things more important for the future of our civilisation, perhaps of the human race itself, than the manner in which what I have called the crucial question is in fact to be ultimately answered. If therefore the author of five or six books was as puzzled as he was flattered by a request for a preface from the author of thirty or forty – with some well-known and well-loved ones among them – he is at least equally delighted by the opportunity it affords him of being present, as it were, at the launching of *The Mystery of Physical Life* and wishing it a heartfelt godspeed.

Owen Barfield
August 1963.

But how if Nature vetoes all
Her commentators? Disenchant
Thy Heart. Look round!

from *Clarel*
Herman Melville.

It will not be long before the
noos here finds its eyes.

P. Teilhard de Chardin.

INTRODUCTION

Since my days at Cambridge as a student of biology, my work as a field naturalist has led me to believe that the Darwinian theory of evolution through chance variations and natural selection is too simple to meet the complicated and evasive patterns that Nature presents.

Like other students at any modern university I was grounded in the accepted dogmas, and for a time believed them, till brought up against the profound scepticism of the Professor of Zoology, Adam Sedgwick. I was horrified when he said, in a confidential talk over a paper I had written for him, that he did not believe in any of the theories of evolution. Archetypal forms of plants and animals were, he said, precipitated. *Precipitated,* he seemed to relish the word; and he added that it was bad form in scientific circles to mention the word *creation*. From these precipitated forms the existing genera and species had come into being through processes of devolution. He stressed that for biologists *facts* were of supreme importance: no theory had yet been put forward that could not be contradicted by groups of facts that refused to fit in. For himself, he looked at the facts, and he advised me, as a young man, to do the same.

The influence of Adam Sedgwick on my life of ideas was coincident with that of Nietzsche's atheistical doctrines. Behind Sedgwick's philosophy was an honest but uninspired desire for knowledge; behind Nietzsche's the glamour of a poetic genius that carried me into a cloud of perplexity and unknowing. Within that cloud, since knowledge had become so uncertain, I sought my way towards some kind of understanding of the facts, which Sedgwick had stressed as important, each object revealing its own wonder.

I read the earlier critics of Darwin's theory, and I read many times and with great admiration, *The Origin of Species*. Against Darwin's meticulously gathered and ordered classes of facts I placed Fabre's animal life-histories, and was duly puzzled. Later the writings of such men as Goethe and Fechner, Jung, Steiner and Bergson, Eddington and Sherrington, and Kohler's Gestalt Psychology opened wide horizons, but did not offer any easily made conclusions. These readings, and many others of more strictly scientific character carried me into realms of speculation but did not in any way decrease the wonder; for, behind the ever-changing forms of living things was the mystery of existence.

I experienced life in the usual ways that men experience living, and had the unusually fortunate opportunity of going as zoologist on a scientific expedition to North West Australia. As the years passed, I became of necessity aware of the nihilistic revolution of our time. Nietzsche had boasted that he was the murderer of God, and that God, as people had come to understand the word, was dead. The idea that God was dying became for many honest and intelligent people only too true, and not because Nietzsche, that fiery psychologist, had killed him with his sledge-hammer, but because Darwin in his gentlemanly and quiet English way had made God superfluous in a philosophy which said that Chance was sufficient to account for the order of living things, as we observe them on earth.

The philosophy that lies behind Darwin's theory has been taught as a dogma in schools and colleges for the last eighty years. It has had a far-reaching effect, since most students believe what they are taught, and some apply their belief to their general outlook, if not to their immediate conduct. The idea prevails that it is proved that men are descended from monkeys. During this time a great de-bunking process had been in operation. The implications which lie within the thought of a world in which no creative principle is either emergent or in process of self-revelation, is such that men are not stimulated to look for meaning in their own lives, or in the life of the universe. The confidence that earlier generations have derived from a belief in God has been largely withdrawn, and this in spite of the religious institutions that still survive. A great dichotomy has been created; science on one side, and orthodox religion on the other. In schools, to the bewilderment of many pupils, they are taught atheism in the Zoological laboratory, and in the chapel, something different.

Darwin has been followed by Freud, who, revealing and valuable as his work has been, has added to the same adriftness that is shared by many people of this generation. This attitude of mind, deriving from the belief in a chance-blown universe, has become the foundation of the rationalistic valuation of all things, from which has stemmed the mechanistic interpretation of our life on earth.

This well-nigh compulsive belief that all things can be measured in units of quantity is a comparatively new development in human thinking, and does not reach back for more than two hundred years. This fashion of thought has separated the exact scientist from the poet, the philosopher and the man of religion. Yet it seems possible that this division may suffer a further change now that the nuclear physicists have dissolved the "reality" of appearances into infinitely minute particles whose position and velocity cannot be observed at the same instant of time, and we have made of the so-solid-seeming earth the "unsubstantial fabric of a dream."

A further revolution of thought is in process, and further orientations suggest that we must augment the quantitative valuations of modern scientific method with imaginative and intuitive qualitative valuations, in order that a wider and less rigid science may come into being. There are signs that the existing gulf between science and the humanities may be reduced.

When in April 1960 I was visiting Dr Jung at Küsnacht, we discussed possible ways of looking for the origin of the patterns in plant and animal behaviour, and in the metamorphosis of growth. He dismissed abruptly the Darwinian idea of evolution through chance and natural selection as being too simple to account for the contradictions in the ways of what he called "The Elfin Goddess of Life". There remain two other possibilities: either there is an emergent impulse which manifests in a developing consciousness linked with an increasing complication in form, something akin to the enteleche of Aristotle and the vitalism of some modern schools; or else there has been, and, continues to be, a descent of the Spirit, as believed by the Gnostics and some of the early Christians. This belief, with considerable modifications, survived in the creeds of the Christian Church throughout the Middle Ages, and still held sway in the minds of men till the advent of the scientific era some two hundred years ago. It postulates, if I may sum it up in the briefest possible manner, a gradual incarnation of the Logos, the Logos being the Words spoken in the Beginning, which contains all potentialities, but which only gradually becomes incarnate, a true *descent* of the Spirit; an objective manifestation of a spiritual environment, as objective and "real" as tables and chairs to our sense-perceptions.

Dr Jung did not commit himself to either of these alternatives, nor did he deny either. He challenged me over the word Logos, but when I suggested that the archetypes in the unconscious were objective spiritual realities, he agreed; but he insisted that they are discovered by empirical methods, appearing out of the unconscious ready-made in the dreams and experiences of modern men, in the same sort of way that people of the Middle Ages discovered angels and demons.

Without going into doctrinal issues, the following essays hover round (if I may use such a phrase) and in some way converge towards, a central consideration, in which plants and animals and humankind present different expressions of such an incarnation. The assumptions involved in such an all-embracing idea offer, as I contend, a more acceptable approach to an understanding of life than either of the other two alternatives.

In attempting to construct such a bridge between the rational and the irrational I am handicapped in two ways; in the first place, such an idea is against the prevalent and strong-flowing desire in men's minds to account for all that they experience in the rationalistic way; in the second place, imaginative and intuitive interpretations have often been associated with much that the evolution of human consciousness has discarded, namely, theological doctrines of various kinds.

My conversation with Dr Jung brought this home to me when I spoke of the descent of the Logos as a possible explanation of the origin of species. He said, you cannot use the terminology of the Church, which has altogether appropriated Christianity, unless you abandon any claim to scientific reasoning; you cannot put new wine into old bottles. If you try to do so you will have a hundred thousand scientists against you, and you will be alone.

I did not answer at the time, for I had not come to see Dr Jung to argue. Afterwards I thought: might it not be possible to make new bottles in which to put the new wine made from the fruits of our modern knowledge, grown on branches grafted on the True Vine, which symbolises the universal creative impulse?

Before I had gone out to Küsnacht, Dr Jung had been kind enough to read some of the following essays; the second essay on the synchronicity of the growth of plants with the Fibonacci series had been, in particular, what had interested him. Of that he had written in a letter to me: "Well, your ideas move in the right direction, Good Luck! Benedictus intelligit."

CHAPTER ONE

THE MYSTERY OF INSTINCT

Science stops at the frontiers of logic, but nature does not–she thrives on ground as yet untrodden by theory.

C. G. JUNG

The number of objects that the human race progressively differentiates in the course of its evolution increases with the growing awareness of men. Human use and experience of objects has culminated in the elaborate techniques of modern science; the world of Nature has been revealed, and the morphological classification of natural species well established; we have a wide picture of all earthly things, and can construct possible frameworks of thought into which our classifications of objects can be fitted.

Should we make the assumption that life, somehow, and at some time has originated on the earth, it is possible to suppose that the chance variations which are found inherent in all species may account for the existing patterns, sufficient time being allowed. Charles Darwin and the majority of biologists who have followed in his steps have supposed that such variations, occurring in all directions, could bring about slow but steady transformations of one species into another. All that was necessary, so they contested, is that the variations should occur in all directions, and that sufficient time for a sufficient number of generations be allowed for the changing influences of environment to act as selective forces, and so promote some variations while discouraging others. The surviving individuals of each generation being those who *by chance* possess the favouring characteristics; these changes having been brought about by the immense prodigality of life, and the consequent struggle for survival.

The idea of such gradual evolution was afloat in men's minds before Darwin published his *Origin of Species* in 1859, and early evolutionists such as Lamarck and A. R. Wallace postulated a life-principle which could influence and order the morphological development in each particular species. It is Darwin's distinction, and possible mistake that he put forward the idea that chance variations, moulded by the changing environment could, unaided by any vitalistic or metaphysical assistance, have produced the animal and plant forms that we find today. In his *Origin of Species Darwin* collected and classified a great many facts which seemed to support this theory. He had his critics at the time of publication and onwards, and not only the churchmen, who maintained that there were other facts which did not easily fit into this framework of thought. Many pertinent criticisms were at that time swamped by the general mental excitement produced by this book. Opinions were largely divided into *pros* and *cons,* and the theory of Evolution through variation and natural selection was accepted by many biologists and by a large number of educated people as a step towards a wider and more realistic valuation of phenomena than that offered by orthodox religions. To an age largely interested in material things, whose energies were so much devoted to controlling natural forces and their subjection to human convenience, the theory of evolution which Darwin advanced was the natural expression of its own urgent activities. The vitalistic theories of A. R. Wallace and Lamarck and the scepticism of Henri Fabre were not so appropriate to the collective psyche of the time as the simple rationalism of Charles Darwin, who asked for only the presence of chance variations and time to account for the multitudinous manifestations of life. Chance and time, both patently present to the senses of the dullest of men, were all that was needed, and any metaphysical or vitalistic urge towards an ordained end savoured too much of wishful thinking. It was Darwin who by clear reasoning and quiet statement became the eliminator of the idea of God in the minds of men.

There have been from time to time revivals of the evolutionary ideas of Lamarck and Wallace, and these in recent times have with stressed and elaborate changes, blossomed in the new humanism, as prepounded by Julian Huxley, and set forth in the vast *Weltanschauung* of Pierre Teilhard de Chardin, who traces the evolution of mind from simple beginnings to the advent of man, who stands on the threshold of individual reflection, at the advent of what de Chardin calls the *noosphere*, a self-rolling wheel of creation capable of self-seeking, self-seeing and even self-renunciating faculties. His book *The Phenomena of Man* may seem far from the simple and less all-embracing theories of the early vitalists, but the same principle of an emergent and ascending consciousness informs them both. This framework of thought may be seen as one capable of explaining the phenomenal world. It has grown up parallel to the Darwinian theory. It does not necessarily admit the atheism implicit in Darwinism, for the *noosphere* as postulated by de Chardin is certainly not the outcome of unaided chance.

The chapters of this present book are set in another framework, one which came into being in the early centuries before Christ and which was elaborated with great thoroughness by early Christian and Gnostic cults, and which in the light of an expanding human consciousness, aware of yet deeper human perceptions, is now discovering evidence of a *descending* spirit, that has, in course of time, found its way into earthly incarnation. This idea, though centuries old, claims the serious consideration of the Modern Man, as being adequate to provide a framework into which can be set the observed facts as conveyed through the senses, our only true guides.

Such a proposition argues in favour of a subjective, and therefore qualitative, as well as objective, quantitative valuations of facts, and in so doing demands that the Modern Man in search of his soul should widen his awareness through making his subjective feeling an object of his scrutiny. In so doing he will enter into *relation* with the creatures of his observation, for in such participation some flavour of the creative, incarnating thought will speak to him, although it will not by any means reveal itself altogether. His silence before the object reveals in an enlightening manner *something* that is not altogether manifest, but that *is*. It blazes into presentness, and as it does so, both subject and object enter into the state from whence it came. When this happens such questions as: What is consciousness? What is instinct? What is music? become relevant. As we question, we observe that they have deep-rooted connections one with another.

In all patterns of instinctive behaviour we notice recurring themes and variations on themes, as in music. These patterns also have the appearance of conscious purpose. Purpose is certainly there, though it may not be present to the awareness of the instinctive creature.

Instinctive behaviour is subdued, or partially subdued, in such semi-conscious creatures as dogs, apes and men; in less conscious creatures such as molluscs and insects it is highly developed. It has been called a tendency towards actions, manifesting an unconscious wisdom which works for the benefit of the creature. By these dry words we betray our remoteness from the vital stream. Theoretical considerations cannot take us to the goal of our quest, for our ultimate goal must lie within the springs of life. Life defies our measurement; only the *properties* of nature can be described in quantitative terms. We can weigh a mouse, and know the length of its ears and tail, but we cannot measure the quality of mousehood.

In our scientific pursuit of the knowledge of quantitative values we have lost much of the spontaneous feeling for the realities of the Spirit. Yet because of our advance in scientific knowledge we know that we cannot dispense with the freedom from false identifications and projections that science has conferred. Modern science has taught us to stand apart, to separate ourselves from the objects of our study, and to be no longer like the primitive, who lives in a state of mystical and all-enfolding participation with Nature; a step in progress not to be retraced. By a further step we cultivate a feeling of *immediacy* between ourselves and what we behold in Nature; participation is no longer mystical and vague, but conscious. Goethe, who cultivated conscious participation in his approach to Nature, called his method, "the creating of exact imaginative fantasy". He tried to look at Nature in her *wholeness*, as she presented herself at any particular moment, and he considered that the merely experimental method of examining detached portions of the works of Nature was of secondary importance.

But how, it may be asked, can we obtain exactness within the vague and ever-shifting framework of unrestricted Nature? Dr C. G. Jung, working partly as an empiricist and partly as an intuitive, has followed Goethe's lead, and has attempted an interpretation of Nature in relation to the human psyche. He demonstrates that, with the enlargement of consciousness, there can be brought to light what Goethe has called a hidden *something* within the subject which corresponds to a hidden *something* in the object. A flash of insight results: it is a momentary illumination of the "now", a new-created reality is present to awareness. William Blake packed this somewhat evasive idea into the terse and forcible saying: "A fool sees not the same tree as the wise man sees."

If with such thoughts as these we look at Nature, we are clearly in a region no longer contained within the strict limits of science. The materialist will not see the same *Paramecium* as the intuitive sees. Scientific knowledge, in the accepted sense of the words, will then appear as the marshalling of facts within an ordered pattern of experimental findings, the establishing of the average and the mean. *Understanding*, however, will be the discovery of the uniqueness of any situation.

In something of this way, accepting the possibilities of mistakes, I have tried in my experience as a field-naturalist to look at the instinctive behaviour of animals, and have felt within the regions of my awareness for a corresponding relatedness, believing that only in so far as this relatedness with the object can be felt, can I achieve understanding, as opposed to mere knowledge. I have become aware of what Dr C. G. Jung has called: "the noumenal *reality* which embraces the whole situation", which includes the observer and the observed. With this idea modern physics has made us familiar. To make clearer what Dr Jung means by the total situation I quote a passage from his book *The Archetypes and the Collective Unconscious*, where he describes just such an experience:

> From a low hill in the Athi plains of East Africa I once watched the vast herds of wild animals grazing in soundless stillness as they had done from time immemorial, touched only by the breath of a primaeval world. I felt then as if I were the first man, the first creature, to know that all this *is*. The entire world around me was still in its primaeval state; without that moment it would never have been. All Nature seeks this goal and finds it fulfilled in man, but only in the most highly developed and most fully conscious man. Every advance, even the smallest, along this path of conscious realisation adds that much to the world.

This consciousness he writes of is one that can grasp some inkling of the noumenal reality, gaining from the transitory *now* of an outer experience an inner and unfading reality.

In the same way that the herds of animals on the Athi Plains can be realised as both outer and inner reality, so can the instinctive patterns of animal-behaviour (seen as totalities within their environment) be illumined, especially when events within their pattern defy the usual and more simple explanation of causality. These enigmatic designs may well become vantage points for further exploration.

Henri Bergson in the introduction to his *Creative Evolution* put forward something of the same thought. He suggests that, "If instinct were articulate, if we could ask it, and it could reply, it would render up to us the most intimate secrets of the Universe." Of one thing we can be certain, that the instinctive behaviour of the creature is in the closest possible relationship with its environment; it is also obvious that such relatedness has been produced in a great variety of life-manifestations. "If these forms of instinctive and seemingly automatic behaviour," Bergson writes, "could be brought together and united with intellect, the result might be as wide as life itself." "Such a synthesised consciousness", he says, "turning round suddenly against the push of life which it feels behind, would have a vision of life complete—would it not? even though that vision were fleeting."

Such is the imaginative speculation that he makes, but it may be questioned: is he suggesting a situation which by its nature is impossible? Can instinct as itself, as instinct, ever be endowed with the self-conscious, critical power of intellect, and so be self-regarding? Western thought, as exemplified by modern biological science, regards instinct as an innate and unpremeditated wisdom which, in its own sphere, manifests a complete, though limited, perfection. In contrast, learning from conscious experiment and consequent reasoning from established facts has some of the assurance of instinctive action. The two would *seem* to be of a different nature.

In Eastern thought and tradition we do not find so clear a cleavage. In past times a form of human self-conscious knowledge grew into being in India which did not proceed from thought, but from a practice of creating irregularities in the breathing system. By these practices, the instinctive and unconscious process of breathing was raised into consciousness. In the *act* of, and by means of the irregulating practices, a process, instinctual in itself, was lifted, and revealed in a superior consciousness, called Yoga. In this way, Bergson's suggestion of a self-regarding instinctive and self-apothesised wisdom may have been achieved.

In Europe the way of advancement is altogether different

from that of the Yogis of Southern Asia in 4000 B.C. Yoga does not grow naturally from our soil. Our thought is directed towards learning from experiment; we observe, and invent theories to bind our observations together. We discover portions of the complicated pattern that life provides; we record facts, and if these cannot find adjustment with current theories, then we let imagination explore, as far as it is able, not only the surface patterns, but so far beyond as it can reach.

From a large number of life-histories that have been recorded by reliable observers, I select only two to furnish material to illustrate the foregoing ideas. Restricted, as so few examples must be, they provide mysteries enough.

In the comparatively shallow waters, between the tides, are to be found various species of sea-slugs. These are for the most part more brightly coloured and more elaborated in shape than slugs that live on the land. Many of them have brilliantly coloured papillae growing from their backs, and on the surface of these papillae are found groups of stinging cells which are believed to function as defensive weapons, protecting the slugs from their natural enemies. It is presumed that fish snap at these brightly coloured appendages rather than at the more vulnerable, sober-hued and vital portions of their victims. The nettle cells discharge in the mouth of the aggressor, thus sending him away discomforted and unlikely to renew the attack.

These nettle-cells, or nematocysts, found on the backs of sea-slugs have a curious history, and one which must certainly provoke questions in the mind of any evolutionist who would maintain that the characteristics of living creatures are in all cases the result either of environmental stimulus or of fortuitous mutations that survive by the operation of natural selection.

When nematocysts were first discovered to be present in the papillae of sea-slugs they excited the interest of biologists, for they suggested a close affinity between the *Mollusca*, to which group the sea-slugs belong, and the group of more simple organisms, the Coelenterata, which includes sea-anemones and jelly-fish. It was previously believed that only coelenterates were provided with nematocysts. The nematocyst is an explosive cell which, in its discharged condition, is usually of a long whip-like shape and provided with various barbs. In its undischarged condition, and this is the condition in which it is formed, it is folded within itself, and is much contracted, its walls being under tension from turgor within. At the least touch from any foreign body the nettle-lash will fly out, its barbs forming weapons of offence or defence. Many sea-anemones and jelly-fish are provided with such protective cells.

The facts of the relationship between the coelenterates and the sea-slugs, and the part that the stinging-cells play in all this, have been carefully explored by marine biologists. It has been found that the nematocysts which lie in an unexploded condition on the outer surface of the papillae of the sea-slugs, and which are used, it is presumed, as a defensive mechanism against their enemies, have their origin in the coelenterates on which the sea-slugs feed.

Many facts have been made known; the interpretation remains obscure. It has been observed how certain species of sea-slugs can devour the tissues of coelenterates that possess poison-dealing nematocysts – but without exploding them. This would seem to be a kind of miracle, for the nematocysts are so conditioned that they explode at the least touch. The touch of the sea-slug is by no means delicate, for, after the habit of all slugs and snails, the harsh saw-like radula tears its food; yet this violence does *not* explode the highly explosive stinging-cells. It has been suggested that the slug, in eating, exudes mucus which prevents the discharge of the nematocyst, but why are not the defensive cells discharged? They are in some cases, but not in all; some favoured species are immune. Mr O. C. Glaser, one of the biologists who has examined the life-cycle of the sea-slugs, writes: "It is truly remarkable that these apparently helpless creatures (the sea-slugs) should have selected such a dangerous prey, but since they have, it must be because the danger does not apply to them. Why it does not, I do not know, but it may well be for the same reason that the nematocyst does not discharge while being eaten."

The immunity of the slug to the nematocyst in the act of eating is but the prelude to a yet stranger story. The unexploded nematocysts are swallowed by the slug and from the gullet they pass down into the stomach, where the other tissues of the coelenterates are digested. Not so the nematocysts. They are gathered together from out of the stomach of the slug and pass into narrow ciliated channels, and are swept by the working of the cilia up into tiny pouches which lie near the periphery of bright coloured papillae. They are here arranged the right way up in symmetrical rows in such a way that they discharge against any intruder that comes in contact with the sea-slug.

Here surely is a highly complicated series of events, which would certainly seem to be directed towards an end-cause. The instinct of the slug directs the slug, in this case, to eat the highly dangerous food. Can the physiological processes that follow also be called instinct? Are all unconscious life-processes a *form of instinct*, as, for example, the workings of a kidney or the unconscious beatings of a heart? If these are of a different nature to instinct, where do we draw the line between the instinctive eating of the dangerous food and the subsequent way in which the slug deals with the dangerous weapons that it is in the process of appropriating? I do not know how any hard and fast line can be drawn, and we must consequently regard instinctive behaviour as one in character with other unconscious life-processes. We may say that either the instinct organises the instruments it is about to use – in the foregoing case the instinct in the slug to eat the dangerous coelenterates – or that the process of organisation (the general physiological build-up) is anticipated in the instinctive behaviour. They are really one.

It may be asked: "Are these facts really true? Surely it is only reasoning and reasonable men who can steal the offensive or defensive weapons of weaker creatures, and use them for their own purpose?"

The sea-slug does steal the stinging-cells of the sea-anemone. G. H. Grosvenor, and subsequently other biologists, have proved that the nematocysts found in the sea-slug and those produced by coelenterates are identical in plan, in construction and in mode of discharge, and that nematocysts of several distinct types occur in each group – also that a single type of nematocyst does not occur uniformly throughout the members of any one species of sea-slug, but that different individuals of the same species will have quite different kinds of nematocysts according to the kind of food they have been eating. They have also shown that a single individual sea-slug may have within the pouches of the dorsal papillae nematocysts of several different types, found in distinct groups of coelenterates; and further, that when it is known on what coelenterates a sea-slug has been feeding, then the nematocysts in the two are identical in type. Moreover they have shown that sea-slugs which feed on animals that have no nematocysts, have themselves no nematocysts. They have also demonstrated the ciliated canals which pass from the diverticulate in the stomach of the slug to the pouches on the dorsal papillae, and have shown that the nematocysts in any particular sea-slug will be changed after a change of diet.

Before hazarding any further speculations on so complicated a relationship, let us look elsewhere at a relation no less complex but quite different.

The fig is in itself a complex flower, a collection of small flowers enclosed within a receptacle. The orifice of this urn-like bunch of flowerlets, or synconium, as it is called, is very small. The flowers fill almost the entire cavity. The female flower consists of a pistil and ovary, containing a single ovule. Some kinds of figs have two different forms of female flowers contained in the same synconium; some with short styles and abortive stigmas. These latter are called gall-flowers, as they are produced for the use and convenience of a small gall-wasp. These gall-flowers are, as a rule placed low down in the synconium, and the male flowers, which consist of only a single stamen, are near the mouth. Some figs contain only single female flowers. These are known as *Ficus*. Those which contain both gall-flowers and male-flowers are called *Caprificus*.

The gall-wasp *Blastophaga grossurum* enters the fig by the orifice, crawls down the inflorescence until it reaches the gall-flowers, and sinks its ovipositor down the style-canal. It lays an egg close to the nucleus of the ovule. The larva of the wasp feeds on the substance of the ovule, which is sufficient for its development.

The male wasps emerge earlier than females. They are wingless. They do not leave the synconium, but visit the galls containing female wasps, which they fertilise while the females are still within the gall. When the females emerge they crawl up the central passage of the synconium, and become dusted with pollen from the male flowers. When the wings of the female have expanded and dried, they seek out inflorescences which are at an earlier stage of development than those from which they have emerged. They crawl into them, and lay their eggs in the ovaries, but they are careful only to select the gall-flowers which have undeveloped stigmas, those which would seem to have been specially provided for them. The true female flowers with long styles are, however, dusted by the pollen. Should the wasp make a mistake (which it is doubtful if it ever does) and lay an egg in a normal female flower, the style is too long for the wasp's ovipositor to reach the ovule. The egg is left at a place unfavourable for further development. The gall-flowers, on the other hand, are well-adapted for the reception of the wasp's egg, and, in this complicated pattern of symbiotic relationship, seem to have been specially provided by the fig for the wasp's convenience. In return for this service, the wasp carries the pollen from one inflorescence to another. Our wonder at this complementary service, the elaborations and the economies, as manifested both by the wasp and the plant, prompts us to question: How could so complicated and perfect reciprocity have come about through the action of natural selection? What unit-characters, both in fig and wasp, could have become so synchronised by chance segregation – even though it be supposed that countless generations may have contributed to such an adjustment?

There are about six hundred species of figs, and more than fifty species of wasps have been observed in this symbiotic relationship. Some species of figs have their own particular species of wasps, others share wasps between them. What is remarkable is that the pattern, though differing in detail, should bear overall resemblances, suggesting that some formative power has been finding its expression in this significant manner.

These examples which have been chosen from hundreds of others as well-established, are hard to interpret. If we think only in terms of the inheritance of unit, chance-instigated characters that have segregated out, both in the slugs and in the coelenterates in synchronising harmony, our human faculties are stretched beyond capacity. It is difficult to conceive how such harmony in two different organisms could have come about. If on the other hand we look at the happenings as constituting a pattern of *wholeness*, we can see these closely bound symbiotic associations as not so much as that of two organisms, but rather of two activities. The life-histories express, in concrete form, the relation of one to the other, and let it be noticed that neither of these examples is unique. The theme is, as in music, a group of many variations set within the limitations of a governing pattern in each case.

I can suggest no comprehensive answer, but can merely describe my own reaction. I try to participate imaginatively with the object of my observation, and at the same time to maintain the greatest possible detachment. I am, of course, not alone in this endeavour. Such participation, it may be objected, would be more becoming in a poet or a philosopher than in a scientist, whose business is analysis and measurement; but must the scientist always be bound to quantitative valuation? Is it not time that qualitative judgments should enter into our scrutiny and so achieve a subjective-objective way of looking at Nature?

It has again and again been possible for naturalists to tune themselves in so that they are in harmony with the creatures of their study. Examples, selected from amongst many of such tunings-in are offered by the relation of Fraser Darling to the seals on Rona, of T. H. White to his goshawk, and of H. S. Jennings to his micro-organisms. Through feeling and imagination, they participate consciously in the lives of the creatures of their study, and grow to anticipate the outward actions that proceed from the inner activities. Through sympathy and antipathy, and through the anguish of the effort, we experience in ourselves something of what is happening in the creature, and so we may, with good fortune, come near the mystery of instinctive life. Within the wholeness of its particular pattern the instinctive animal is at-one with all that makes its environment. As I have said, the patterns of the group-activities are like musical themes. They are often repeated, and we see that it is not only one species of sea-slug that has the power to devour and turn to its own use the nematocysts of coelenterates, but several species can do so. Not one species of wasp, or one species of fig, but several conform to the *Caprificus* pattern.

In all theories of Evolution, or in theories of Creation, assumptions are made. Men have never been able to say that they know for sure. We can only observe, and make what seem reasonable assumptions into which our observations will fit. If the observations do not fit, then we abandon our assumptions. It was assumed by philosophers from Plato to Hegel that all natural objects are the expression of Thought. Not only theologians and philosophers have had this idea. The German naturalist, Henrik Stefans, suggested that animals are "fixed ideas incarnate". Such a statement implies that behind the incarnation there is a formative idea. By calling this fixed, he assumes that the idea has become rounded off and fixed within the limitation of the species. It has, as it were, been jettisoned from the onward moving stream of evolution. It remains in a set pattern of physiological and instinctive activity. About the formative idea he says nothing. Professor Whitehead in *Process and Reality* has touched on the same thought. "No biological science has been able to express itself apart from phraseology, which is meaningless unless it refers to *ideas* proper to the organism in question." In contradiction to this, the mechanistic hypothesis attempts to describe the world of living things as existence without meaning.

When we experiment under arbitrary conditions, the creatures of our experiments are depleted. Pavlov's dogs in the sound-proof, light-regulated cells are no longer dogs; they are reduced to the mechanism that the instinct of the dog uses for its purposes. The aim of Science is the *wholeness* of Nature. The instinctive is fundamental. If instinct could be endowed with self-regarding intelligence, it would say: I and my environment are one. The sea-slugs and their strange relatedness to the coelenterates, and all the other etceteras of their environment, are parts of an organic activity. The fig-wasp, the fertile flowers and strangely adventitious gall-flowers are also an organic wholeness, within the limitations of their particular pattern.

With such thoughts in mind, although they give no ultimate solution, we take an initial step towards a qualitative valuation of life. This is not out of step with other sciences. The physicists have analysed the nature of matter, and have come to see the physical world as conditioned by human consciousness. Professor A. S. Eddington in the last chapter of *Space, Time and Gravitation* sums up his conclusions.

We have found that where science has progressed the furthest, the mind has but regained from nature what the mind has put into nature.

We have found a strange foot-print on the shore of the unknown. We have devised profound theories, one after another, to account for its origin. At last we have succeeded in reconstructing the creature that makes the foot-print. And Lo! it is our own.

Our perceptions have in the first place been conditioned by our attempts to find our physical equilibrium, when, as infants, we learned to walk upright. Within our physical being our geometry was born; our faculty of thinking finds again in matter the mathematical properties which our faculty of perceiving has already deposited there. Consequently we see the outward world yield with docility to our reasoning. So far as we can approach reality, what we find intelligible is of our own making. Of reality, itself, we know nothing, and are not likely to know more than its reflection in the symbols that are mysteriously presented to our senses. The intellectuality of the mind and the materiality of things are two sides of an equation, for in a general way, what we perceive is, in degree, conditioned by our capacity of perception. The order that we discover is a reflection of our own development; the mind finding itself again in things.

The casually accepted outward form is not sufficient; we seek the unknown content, what Eddington has called the stuff of our consciousness, reflected back in our discoveries.

The biology of the future may well be the discovery of correspondences; it may come to see that the instinctive life of the lower animals, where instinct is so precise and limited, is co-respondent to the as-yet unconscious physiological functions of the human body, where, within the working of the will, the continuous process of building up and tearing down constitutes the very existence, and the anguish of that existence, hidden from us by its unconscious nature.

Instinct and physiological function are closely allied. Where does the one finish and other begin? Sir Charles Sherrington in his closely reasoned work *Man on his Nature* sums up in the last chapter. Man, he suggests, can look into the stream of his being, seeing it as, in part, objective to his perceiving mind. Unlike the instinctive creature, that Bergson has postulated, he sees, within the physiological urges, a mechanism that science can apprehend, what he calls "a Purpose and a guiding Hand". It may seem surprising that he should have written the words with capital letters. Within the shell of outer-seeming, he guesses a content.

At the vanishing periphery of sense-perception we touch the nouminous, from which instinctive actions proceed. Instinct guides the actions of the sea-slugs and the fig-wasps; it appears to flow non-casually, and has so far defied the meticulous investigations of bio-genetics. We see it as something unselfconscious, as though it slept – and dreamed. Our task is to enter into the dream of Nature and interpret the symbols.

CHAPTER TWO

IMAGINATIVE FANTASY

I only make progress because I make a leap in faith.

EINSTEIN

So waiting I have won from you the end, God's presence in each element.

GOETHE

Men, in all ages, have been interested in trying to find signs of order in the universe. Looking at the world, that portion of the universe with which we are most immediately concerned, we observe various kinds of things that can be naturally grouped into classes. The most striking division is between the living and the non-living. There are border-line cases, complicating simple definitions. For example, we may say that the characteristic of living organisms is that they grow. But crystals grow in saturate solutions. Crystals cannot be said to be alive, and it is not easy in any universal and comprehensive way to define life. We vaguely know what we mean by being alive. We know how to recognise the majority of living things, and to distinguish them from the non-living. For the present let us neglect the border-line cases, and following a method of induction, work from the particular to the general.

If we look at a stone or a crystal of quartz, we see that it has an enduring quality, that it changes very slowly. It has a physical body that we can handle, measure and weigh. In the case of unstable minerals such as sodium, change is easily provoked, but, having changed, the resulting compound tends to assume a static condition. If now we compare a stone or crystal with some well-established plant such as a wallflower or a potato, we will see that the plant also has a physical body, but that it is subject to quick changes, that it grows from a seed, expands to stem and leaves, flowers, sets seeds for the next generation, withers and dies: a cycle of germination, growth, flowering, seed-setting and decay. The plant would seem to have certain faintly-indicated "desires", in that it disposes its leaves in a definite way, so that they may expand to get a maximum of sunlight. The plant follows a predestined pattern which, unless altered by external or internal stimuli, accords with the nature of the species. Within the life-cycle, death is an inevitable part. The crystal, on the other hand, after it has accomplished the initial growth remains as it is through centuries of time. The plant, looked at in this way, would seem to possess something that the crystal has not. It obviously possesses a physical body, but it has something else. This something else, we call, by a fairly general consent – life. Added to physical body of the inert crystal the *something else* that the plant has is life.

If now we compare a plant with an animal – our wall-flower with a cat or a blackbird, we will notice that the animal or bird has, besides a physical body and the quality of life, a highly developed desirousness. We only have to look at a cat with but a little imagination, and we see that it is formed for the satisfying of desires. It lives enveloped within an atmosphere of desires. To a touch on the back it rises in a sensuous response. Its night-time voice, so terrible and perplexing, is the very utterance of desires. It has in its constitution something that the plant has not. It has a physical body, it has life, and it has desires.

A man has all of these, but he has something extra, he has reflective consciousness and a faculty of learning. Animals have a certain amount of reflective consciousness, but not so much as a man. A cat is quite aware of the confines of its body, a duck is not so sure, but no animal has the same power of memory as a man. An animal can recognise a situation that it has known before, and in this sense it has a memory, but it can never say to itself: "Last Thursday, I did such a thing, and next Thursday I will do the same." It does not have the intense conviction that can come to man who can say: "I, in separating myself in conscious awareness from the things of the world, am of unique existence, able to value and name all things." The man has something extra to the animal.

In this way we can classify the things that we perceive: –

Minerals, and with them, gases and liquids, have a physical body in which the changes, slow or fast, work towards a something static and unchanging.

The plant has, besides the physical body, life.

The animal has a physical body, life and desire.

Man has all that the animal has, and the something extra, which we call ego-consciousness. The I AM, the same perhaps that Moses heard from the burning bush, and that Christ may speak of when he said: "I am the bread which has come down from heaven."

This classification I do not put forward with a claim to any originality, but I suggest it may help to illumine facts. It is a qualitative classification. By the nature of things, not a great many facts can be scrutinised in a comparatively small book; but, limited as they are, it is inevitable that they will fit one framework better than another. Never must it be forgotten that any framework of thought must be tested again and again in relation to its ability to accommodate the facts.

Besides the power of growth, living things are distinguished from the non-living by being able to take into their system material differing both chemically and physically from themselves, and to incorporate it, in changed form, into their own bodies. Both plants and animals do this in their differing and complementary ways. The processes of growth are partially understood, and much more is known about cell-division and the building of tissues, yet the impulse that causes the growth remains hidden in mystery.

To gain some hints as to what is known and what remains unknown, the study of phyllotaxis in plants provides a field not too large, yet having much to provoke our wonder.

In 1914, Theodore Cook published in his *Curves of Life* an

elaborate description of the spiral curves that enter into all forms of growth, from that of the minutest micro-organism to the great astro-nebulae of the heavens. The spiral is found in the structure and organ-distribution of plants, in shells and in bones, the horns of animals and in the artistic works of man. In plastic works of art it appears not only in the obvious curves, but in the ratio of one part to another. The date of publication is significant, for at the same time as Cook conceived his ideas about the curves of growth, and hinted cautiously at a metaphysical determinant, Dr Jung was beginning to think *about archetypes* as unconscious, a-priori determinants of imagination and behaviour, reaching a conscious preception in the human mind, chiefly in the form of mythological and dream images. In his *Psychology of the Unconscious*, published in 1917, he spoke of "*urtümliche Bilder*", primordial images. Cook anticipated, in tentative manner, the idea that archetypal form should be considered as prior to the undifferentiated primal force; or rather, that the primal force of energy, although appearing, as so often, to our dim perceptions as undifferentiated, was not in itself *per se* undifferentiated, but in those cases of spiral growth, so universally found in all living things, was in close approximation to a definite mathematical formula. His suggestion was that this formula, or something near, though not exactly corresponding, was what Dr Jung called "archetypal". Cook contended that while the formulae does not give any clue to what *causes* the forms of life, it does come near to expressing what is *seen*, and, furthermore, that what is seen corresponds to the subjective ideas formed within the mind of the observer. For example, the position that leaves are seen to occupy on a plant-stem are exceedingly close to the curve that is traced by a mathematical formula. That the form which emerges from the growing tissue of the plant should so closely correspond to a mathematical formula appeared to Cook as significant.

Where in the structure of the emergent form are we to look

for its inception? If we are to find it in some *material*, it would be reasonable to suppose that the growing area might reveal it. But when we look at the growing-points of the plant where the new members are about to be formed, there is nothing material to be seen. The primordia are invisible until they show themselves at their appointed places, and so exact is the position of their appearance that it is difficult to imagine that they should arise in any other place. The facts of development seem to justify the assumption that form is precedent to the energy, or contained within the energy that prompts the growth. The energy is *not* undifferentiated, but is, even in its earliest expressions, differentiated in a way that as yet eludes our perceptions of the changes within the material at the growing-points. As for example, the arrangement of leaves on the stems of growing plants – these illustrate a spiral sequence which conforms to a definite mathematical formula.

In temperate climates the leaves turn their uppersides towards the sky so that they may receive both light and dew on the surface of each leaf. The position of the leaves on the stem is such that the one above covers the one below as little as possible. The arrangement of the leaves thus provides open spaces through which sunlight and air can penetrate. This arrangement of the leaves on a stem is called phyllotaxis; it varies with different species of plants, but always conforms to the same formula. A convenient way of measuring the different arrangements is by noticing where two leaves on an ascending stem exactly overlap each other. If the number of leaves between is written as the denominator of a fraction, then the number of turns round the stem it is necessary to make to get from a lower leaf to the one exactly overlapping should be written as the numerator of the fraction. This fraction gives what is called the phyllotaxis-ratio of the plant. For example, in the privet, where the leaves are set in pairs, and each pair is at right angles to the pair below, we count two leaves before reaching the overlapping leaf, and go once round the stem. The ratio is 1/2. In other plants we find other forms of phyllotaxis: 1/3, 2/5, 3/8, 5/13 and 8/21. It will be noticed that the numerator of any of these fractions can be obtained by adding together the numerators of the two preceding terms of the series, and the denominators of any term by adding together the denominators of the preceding terms. Thus 2/5 is 1 plus 1 over 2 plus 3. This series was first recognised by Leonardo of Pisa (Fibonacci) in the thirteenth century – and is most simply expressed as 1, 2, 3, 5, 8, 13, 21, 34, etc. The ratio between the succeeding terms changes as the series advances, the variations becoming less, and the resulting ratio becomes ever nearer to 1·6183398876. This number has been represented by the Greek letter ϕ. It is unique, in that when the terms are arranged in ascending powers of ϕ, ϕ^1, ϕ^2, ϕ^3, ϕ^4, etc., the sum of any two consecutive terms equals the next term.

This mathematical formula is, one might say, the magic formula to which the growth of all things approximates. Phyllotaxis, which we are considering, is one of the simplest examples that may be demonstrated. The members of a plant, leaf or shoot take up on the stem positions that give a minimum of overshadowing, and a maximum of exposure to light and air. The fact that the Fibonacci numbers correspond to the growing impulses of the higher plants was first observed by the German botanists, Schimper and Braun, in 1830. They noted that the spiral sequence of leaves 2/5 produced, between successive leaves, an angle of 144°; in a 3/8 sequence the angle was 135°; in a 5/13 sequence the angle 138°; in a 8/21 sequence, the angle was 137·5°, and they calculated that as the fractional divergence increased, the angle would get ever nearer and nearer to the ideal angle of 137° 30′ 28″. This they called the Fibonacci angle.

Of this relation between a mathematical formula and the natural disposition of plant members on a stem, Cook writes: "This mathematical ratio might have no bearing on botany itself; but the fact remains that these Fibonacci members of the spiral rows of a plant-shoot, that they cannot be wholly meaningless or accidental. Thus, flowers are commonly 3, or 5, parted; the scales of pine-cones 5, 18, or 13, curved series; the curved series of a daisy disk are 21, 34, while there are 13 green involucre leaves on the back of the capitulum; on a sunflower disk the rows of flowerlets may be 34 and 55, or in the finest heads 89 and 144. It is impossible to avoid these facts, or the assumption that the occurrence of such numbers in the case of a spirally constructed system bears a definite relation and has to do with the Fibonacci, or ideal angle of 137° 30′ 28″. In other words, the fact that plants express their leaf arrangements in terms of Fibonacci numbers so frequently that it passes for the normal case is proof that they are aiming at the utilisation of the Fibonacci angle, which will give minimum superposition and maximum exposure to their assimilating members."

The Curves of Life was published in 1914, more than fifteen years before Kohler's *Gestalt Psychology*. There is little doubt that if Cook had had the opportunity of familiarising himself with the ideas of *Gestalt*, he would have been bolder in affirmation, firmer in his argument, which often wavers as though afraid of his thesis. His book *The Curves of Life* presents a full description of the spiral curves that are not only in all living things, but whose mathematical representation, the Fibonacci ratio, or *sectio aurea*, is in close relation to all the works of man, and, he hints that *an idea* is responsible for the principles governing both acts of human creation and natural growth.

Dr Wolfgang Kohler, in his *Gestalt Psychology*, is almost exclusively concerned with the *how* of perception; Cook, with observation. Both authors suggest a pattern, the one of growth, the other of perception. This pattern is built up, in the one case, within the direct perception of the subject, and in the other case is observed as originating within the growth of the organism. On the one hand we have a physical "movement" (gestalt); on the other, a movement within the process of growth. Such parallelisms have not been enough marvelled at. The Fibonacci series is self-evident and, as a series of whole numbers, it exists independently of empirical facts. The periodicity of a biological spiral occurs in nature without the help of mathematical reasoning, unless one *assumes* a process in the growing plant similar to that in the human mind; a coincidence of consciousness and creation. Or to put this another way: the energy or whatever we choose to call the primodial principle, manifests in all moving bodies, the inner psychical movement included. St John may have meant this when he said: "By him all things were made, and without him was not made anything that was made, in him was life; and the life was the light of man." Light, according to this suggestion, is consciousness. The situation within the psyche is no simple situation, and we make a big assumption when we suppose that the quantitative methods of modern science will be able to perceive the whole truth of what is within the growth patterns of Nature.

Kohler in *Gestalt Psychology* argues at considerable length and with great erudition that perception, percept by percept, does not hold true. He criticises other schools of psychologists, such as Behaviourists and Introspectionists. Percepts, he contends, do not present themselves to consciousness one by one, but appear as emotional patterns, ready made, in what he calls *gestalt* formations. These rise in man or animal as *insight*. A patterned mosaic springs into being in the most elementary of concepts. They are not only quantitative but qualitative. The pattern, and not the unit-percept, is in our conscious, and even in our half-conscious, perceptions.

What I am suggesting is that the inner pattern of perception in the individual, as Kohler discovers it, is comparable to the unseen but emergent determinant that is intrinsic in the pattern of physical growth. This, I believe, is illustrated both in the subjective apperception of the ϕ ratio, and in the growing points as revealed in phyllotaxis. I suggest that Kohler's "mosaic" of perception is qualitative, and that his analysis of how we perceive *augments* the quantitative method that is so generally followed in modern scientific investigation.

It is undeniable that the quantitative method, which has been the way of scientific discovery for the last three hundred years, has emancipated the minds of men in so far as it has delivered them from the mystical participation of the savage. Modern man now finds himself increasingly detached from the outer world; he strives to regard all things objectively, to measure and to weigh. In doing so, he looks on Nature in a one-sided way. In striving to measure all things, even the impulses of his behaviour, he has made hollow and empty the very structure of his own life.

It is unthinkable that we should *want* to revert to the mystical participation of the savage, yet if we follow the quantitative methods of modern science, both outer and inner worlds become more and more arid. What is to be the solution of this enigma?

Dr Jung in one of his later books *The Undiscovered Self*, writes:

> Since scientific knowledge not only enjoys universal esteem, but in the eyes of the modern man, counts as the only intellectual and spiritual authority, understanding the individual obliges me to commit *lese-majesté,* so to speak, to turn a blind eye to scientific knowledge. This is a sacrifice not lightly made, for the scientific attitude cannot rid itself so easily of its sense of responsibility. And if the psychologist happens to be a doctor who wants not only to classify his patient scientifically but also to understand him as a human being, he is threatened with a conflict of duties between two diametrically opposed and mutually exclusive attitudes, of knowledge on the one hand, and understanding on the other. This conflict cannot be solved by an either/or, but only by a

kind of two-way thinking; doing one thing while not losing sight of the other.

In view of the fact that, in principle, the positive advantages of *knowledge* work specifically to the disadvantage of understanding, the judgment resulting therefrom is like to be something of a paradox. Judged scientifically the individual is nothing but a unit which repeats itself *ad infinitum*, and would be just as well designated with a letter of the alphabet. For understanding, on the other hand, it is just the unique human being who, when stripped of all those conformities and regularities so dear to the heart of the scientist, is the supreme and only real object of investigation.

In the above passage Dr Jung clearly designates *scientific knowledge* as concerned with quantitative values, the *understanding* as being concerned with qualitative values. He suggests a two-way thinking, doing one thing while not losing sight of another, which I take to mean *understanding*, while yet keeping knowledge in view.

Our problem rests on the word understanding. For understanding there must be participation, but if scientific knowledge is to be kept in view, the participation will not be the mystical participation of the savage, but a conscious, deliberate and imaginative participation. William Blake in his trenchant way of speaking got near the heart of the matter when he said: "I look through, not with my eyes." Should he look merely with the sense-organ that records a surface fact, he sees but an image; but, with imaginative perception, he finds within the object qualities which correspond to something within himself that *awakes* in the recognition of the object.

This idea has been interestingly elaborated by Mr Owen Barfield in his book, *Saving the Appearances*, in which he distinguishes a conscious and deliberate participation from the mystical participation of the savage.

In something the same way, the botanist looking at the

mysterious precision in which buds or leaves appear on the stems of plants, discovers (since he is not, like the primitive, excluded from a sideways glance at knowledge) an ordered, but also mysterious something within himself, a mathematical formula which comes near to coinciding with the pattern Nature presents.

Dr Jung, commenting on this coincidence of the outer event and the inner subjective idea, discloses the depths of speculation that can be opened when we compare such coincident happenings with synchronising events in time. He writes (in a letter: February, 1956):

> The coincidence of the Fibonacci numbers with plant life is a sort of analogy with synchronicity in as much as the latter consists in the coincidence of a physical process with an external physical event of the same character or meaning. But whereas the *sectio aurea* is a static condition, synchronicity is a coincidence in time, even of events that, in themselves are not synchronous (f.i., a case of precognition). In the latter case one could assume that synchronicity to be a property of energy, but in so far as energy is equal to matter it is a secondary effect of the primary coincidence of mental and physical events (as in the Fibonacci series). The bridge seems to be formed by the *numbers*. Numbers are just as well *invented* as they are *discovered* as natural facts, like all true archetypes. As far as I know archetypes are perhaps the most important basis for synchronistic events.
>
> I am afraid this is all very involved and rather difficult, I don't see my way yet out of the jungle. But I feel that the root of the enigma is to be found probably in the peculiar properties of the whole numbers. The old Pythagorean postulate!

To turn from these difficult thoughts, which are so germinal when applied to the mystery of physical life, to the comparatively simple and unimpeded method of growth in phyllotaxis, we see that it reveals in any particular species of plant, a constant pattern. If, however, we consider the growth of a gall, we find strange variations in the growth-pattern, which are imposed on the plant by the presence of a foreign body. In the case of the witch's broom, resemblance to the original habit of the plant remains, but is deformed. In the case of the oak-apple a new kind of growth, different from anything in the original tree, is produced. A new idea is introduced by the presence of the insect. The interior of the oak-apple, which nourishes the grub, is not conditioned by the strict form as is the rest of the oak tree; but, although contained within its limiting rind, it will make new tissue to replace any that is eaten by the grub. In somewhat like manner, though in more complicated patterns, the other forms of galls mentioned in the last chapter, produce elaborate cups, disks, cones, and the likenesses of fruits and carpels which are found in other and diverse species of plants. Although these are difficult for us to imagine, other directive principles of growth are introduced, or seem to be introduced, by the presence of the parasite.

And here it is relevant to my theme to give a short account of the work of a mathematician, the late Mr George Adams, who has turned his attention to the study of the growing plant. The groundwork (if I may call anything so unusual to our accustomed thought a groundwork) is a theory of negative space. Mr Adams is not alone in being interested in the mathematics of negative space. I am no mathematician or physicist, but I have been for some years interested in some of the ideas that I have been able to receive from George Adams' work. On one occasion I saw on his wall a number of diagrams. One of them had a striking resemblance to a Trilobite; the sort of trilobite that a modern artist might draw. Another resembled a Zoea larva. I remarked on these resemblances. Mr Adams, who knew little of Zoology, said these were the projections into negative space of cubes and tetrahedrons.

Indeed, is that really so! The idea came:– perhaps trilobites and zoea larva and other primitive forms of life are projections *out of* negative space of geometric thoughts into our space (which we have come to think of through long association as "positive").*

I will not attempt any detailed description of Mr Adams' work, but shall instead give a short review of his book *The Living Plant*.

He follows Goethe's scientific method, believing that by an exact imaginative perception a man may be able to interpret the language of phenomena, and that there is something in the object, ordered and unknown, which corresponds to a something in the subject. The normal plant is rooted in the earth; its movements are slow and silent. Throughout the cycle of its growth it is influenced by the movements of sun, moon, planets and stars. It rises towards the zenith, unfolds in spiral sequence its leaves, which obey the movements of the containing cosmos. The tip of the leading stem is not, as one might expect, a convex surface, but it is concave, and forms an easily seen hollow space, and this is sometimes more pronounced by the budding leaves that cluster about it, making the cup-shape more obvious. This is not always the rule, but is most frequently the case. The flowers that spring from the terminal shoots are in the form of cups, or are developed from cup-forms which have been adapted in one way or another to the needs of reproduction. In the case of the terminal shoot which does not end in a flower, so long as the shoot is growing, the hollow space is there.

Goethe in his botanical studies, and indeed in all his scientific work, is seeking in the objects of his scrutiny the meaning of their existence. He defines three cycles of expansion in the typical plant.

* In relation to this suggestion, Dr Jung has written:

"The psyche (partially at least), non-spatial and non-temporal, therefore *a-causal*. Your projection from non-space is indeed interesting and exciting."

Against this Dr Jung has written:

"akin to my attempt to let numbers speak themselves."

One. The unfolding of successive leaves and successive side-shoots; these have their origin in the hollow space above the stem-tip.

Two. The unfolding of the flower which is preceded by a phase of contraction in flower-bud and calyx. This second expansion is not a mere process of growth as is the first, but a revealing of the essence, the end-meaning of the plant.

Three. An expansion not from the concave, but a filling of the concave with the convex shape of fruit or seed. The hitherto cup-like gesture of the flower is now filled with material substance. In this way the plant can be seen as a living entity, carrying the secret of its existence within the phases of its transformation.

By such method of thought we seek to approach the meaning of life itself. Neither by the study of morphology, nor of physiological processes alone (though these should not be neglected) but by what Goethe has called *an exact imaginative fantasy*, may we hope to come near the quality of living things. Morphology and physiology can give us quantitative evaluations, but the characteristic of true thinking about living entities is that the observer actually enters into the object in an intuitive way; he lives it, he becomes it, he obtains an understanding of it (though this may be but partial) from the inside, in so far as the correspondence within himself is kindled into recognition. It is only through living in the fullest way that man is capable of apprehending the creative urge which has brought into being the mystery of physical life. We cannot come near to life, or to the mystery of existence, by merely thinking about *things*. The deepest form of reality resides in *life*. (By that I do not exclude death, which is part of the rhythm of life.) In life we are in the presence of something which transcends the material form. Life leads us into the region of what has been vaguely named spirit; by thinking about life, rather than about things, we enter into the spiritual world. The analytical, quantitative approach of modern science has barred man from the perception and recognition of the spiritual. The spiritual is qualitative, never merely quantitative.

Mr Russell W. Davenport in his book *The Dignity of Man* has written on this theme as follows:

> Philosophy cannot fail to face this problem because it is being pushed into it by the scientific revolution, which has carried the technique of thinking about things beyond the intelligible horizons of the very things it is thinking about. Abstraction has abstracted away all reality. It is possible to guess that in the interstices of the atom, as well as in the majestic infinitudes of intergalactic space, the physical sciences have come face to face with the spiritual without knowing what it is, or how to think about it at all. It vanishes before them into high abstractions.

Such thoughts are relevant to our consideration of the mystery of physical life, for it is into this region of the spiritual that Mr George Adams carries his speculations about the living plant. In the realm of the spirit will be found a true interpretation of the phenomena of living forms, and these, he believes, to be related to mathematical ideas about different kinds of spaces derived from modern projective geometry.

For more than a hundred years mathematicians have been familiar with the idea of a space of more than three dimensions. Other kinds of space than Euclidean space can be logically thought of as existing coincidently with Euclidean space, and to-day the forms of space are thought of as the ideal outcome of the forces and entities concerned. Our world of Euclidean space, which we are all accustomed to accept, is not the only world which the mathematician acknowledges as having a logical existence of its own. He conceives the possibility of other spaces coincident with this, and, perhaps, determining the forces and entities which we find in this, our own and accustomed Euclidean space. Since the phenomena of life appear in and about the material body, the prevailing idea is that the innermost structure of matter must somehow contain the key to the appearance of living things – or else, if it does not, the key is not to be found. When the biologist has gone so far as the microscope will take him, he looks to physics and chemistry for explanation. We witness the work of modern embryologists who are always looking for a chemical substance to explain the mystery of growth. In so doing they are pinning their faith on a quantitative analysis of phenomena. Although their initial intention was to study the wonderful regularities of pattern in the forms of living things directly apprehended by the senses, they have been driven into a realm in which the quality of the object of study is replaced by a quantitative analysis. This is the general rule which holds modern science in its paralysing grip.

There are signs, however, of a change. Modern developments in pure mathematics promise a more direct relation to the organic realm. Adams refers to the works of Bavink, Friedmann and Neergaard. Bavink has suggested that in time to come we shall no longer treat Biology as a special branch of Physics, but, on the contrary, the latter will appear as a limiting and degenerate state, in the mathematical sense, of the former. Concepts of quantity and magnitude will take second place. The fundamental notion will be the idea of form. Neergaard defines *Gestalt* as "a totality which determines all its elements or parts, and, vice versa, is determined by them."

In a deeper sense this change of outlook is contained in the later works of Rudolf Steiner, who affirms that we can train our imaginative faculties to become instruments of cognition no less conscious and exact than mathematical reasoning. Our *Gestalt*, our form, our very early existence, is, in the ultimate analysis, identical with our mathematical thought-forms – such as the three perpendicular axes of geometry. Such thoughts have their origin in the form of the human body which we discovered in babyhood when we learned to stand and walk. All our cognitional faculties are thus a sublimation of the powers of life and growth, and are our *Gestalt* in the sense in which Neergaard defines the term. Such an idea of vice versa relationship between the totality of parts, the subject and the object can bring an enhancement to our scrutiny of objects, and to the enlargement of our consciousness. In this way we approach a qualitative perception of the macroscopic phenomena of life and form, instead of only admitting the mathematical thought-forms of the physicist and the chemist via the microscopic and atomic structure.

Adams has much to say, in a highly condensed form, about the qualitative and imaginative approach to the living plant. This imaginately discerned picture he relates to the idea of a negative space, which exists coincidently with Euclidean space, and forms together with it, and with the observing subject, the gestalt pattern of growth. His thesis and his conclusion is that modern projective geometry leads to conceptions closely analogous to Goethe's concept of archetypes. The life-forms which we perceive in Nature are determined not only within Euclidean space, which we take for granted, but by its polar opposite, which we think of as a negative space, a type of space-formation, not a single universal-space given once and for all. He contends that there is evidence to support the idea that spaces of this type come into being and pass away again with the life-processes of living creatures and their several organs. His book is devoted to supplying such evidence. Wherever there is a living seed or a germinating point, whether within the watery substance of the living body, or hovering outside it (as at the growing point of a plant), there is focal contact with another space-formation.

This is the theory which Adams propounds, and if our habits of thought find it too uncongenial and strange to be lightly accepted, then we may say: "The mystery of life is incomprehensible, wonder beyond wonder, yet knowledge grows; and far behind follows a halting understanding." Perhaps such a theory, which Adams firmly claims as scientific Theory of Knowledge, may lead us towards a truth. The sense-perceived object remains dumb and inarticulate until it is united with, and unfolded within, the human act of imaginative perception.

CHAPTER THREE

SOME PATTERNS OF ADAPTATION

Marx substituted economics for metaphysics—the proletarian and peasant for the philosopher and the poet. He brought to the theory of political evolution the same element of orderly inevitability which Darwin had introduced into biology. The Darwinian and the Marxian theories are strictly comparable in the ruthlessness with which they subordinate human nature and human happiness to the working of a scientific principle.

E. H. CARR

Adam Sedgwick used the word "precipitated", and associated it with archetypal forms; he all-too-easily swept aside the idea of gradual evolution. His ideas were question-marks, not to be easily accepted; yet often in the following years they came back to me as I became acquainted with the numerous perplexing cases of symbiotic relationship that Nature offered. Were these precipitated, created, or evolved? There were so many diverse and fantastic patterns; how had these things come to be? Life in many variegated forms was to be found everywhere; in the great depths of ocean, in the floating plankton of the sea-surface, in the salt-pans of deserts, in mountain lakes, and even in the dark depths of the water-filled necks of extinct volcanoes. At its most profuse and variegated it abounded in the shallow waters where land and ocean meet. To every biologist the unexpected associations of animals must come as surprise and question mark. How can these things be? and Why?

There are several species of small fishes which find home and protection from their enemies within the bells of large medusae. The jelly-fish, a very primitive animal indeed, with only the slightest sense of its location, which floats in the upper streams of ocean, has for its own protection long streaming tentacles, armed with stinging-cells which explode at the least touch, inflicting severe stings – as all bathers in tropical waters have learnt to their cost. Associated with the medusae are the small fishes which can go in and out and to and fro, and are not stung by the stinging-cells with which they are often in contact. They appear to be immune to this danger, and will retreat within the bell when threatened by their enemies, who are not immune to the protective stinging-cells. Whether the fishes are of any advantage to the medusae is not known. They do not appear to be so. The medusae are no doubt of advantage to the fishes, and it is remarkable that resting inside the bell of the medusae they are not digested.

Another association which it is not easy to imagine having arisen as the result of a gradual evolution is provided by hermit crabs and their curious relationship with sea-anemones. The hermit crab, which is preyed on by various kinds of fishes, seeks to hide itself, and one of its ways of doing so is to detach a sea-anemone from its seat on the rocks and place it on its own shell, holding it carefully in its pincers till it has taken hold on its new seat. Being thus covered by the medusae it is less likely to be seen by any prowling skate or other fish which can crunch into fragments the whelk shells in which the hermit crabs have made their homes.

If a hermit crab is kept in an aquarium with sea-anemones, an anemone will often be seen to abandon its position on a rock and, gliding towards the crab, will fasten on its shell.

Another such case of association between crabs and sea-anemones is that of a small crab which frequents coral reefs. This crab has small and delicate chelipeds which are of little use to him for attack or defence. The fingers of these claws are armed with recurved teeth, enabling them to take firm hold on the bodies of small anemones. Carefully the crab detaches the anemones from their rock, first one and then another. Clasping them one in each claw, the crab holds them in close proximity to its mouth. The anemones do not appear to suffer from this treatment, and continue to spread their tentacles and to capture any small creatures that are wafted to them in the water. The crab with its first pair of walking legs removes any tit-bit that it fancies from the tentacles of the anemone, and eats it. In this way it uses another creature as a weapon for its own use, and is seldom met without one or two anemones in its claws. The association is common to the species and is not only developed in individual crabs.

Are we to assume that some chance modification of the chelipeds prompted some ancestral crab to detach, as a mere experiment, an anemone, and by chance hold it near its mouth! Must we assume that by chance some creature was caught in the tentacles, and the crab was not slow to take advantage of such good luck, and so retained its hold on the anemone? If we follow up such a line of reasoning, we must assume that the ancestral crab passed on to its offspring a tendency to use their chelipeds in like manner.

There is a small species of Crab also found on coral reefs. The female is considerably larger than the male, who is about the size of a mustard grain. The female crab settles herself on a frond of branching coral in the axil between twigs. By her presence she disturbs the natural growth of the coral, which sends out several smaller twigs than usual in various directions. These are directed by the combined influence of the crab and the parent plant to form a small sphere to enclose the crab in what looks something like one of those little Chinese carvings, where one globe is enclosed within another. In this sphere are a number of holes through which water can pass, bearing small particles on which the crab can feed. She has now become a prisoner – in a prison which she herself has caused to be made. She is also protected, for her prison might be considered as a fortress with hard coralline walls.

The holes through which her food, air and water supply come are large enough to admit her diminutive mate. He can enter and fertilise her and then depart, although she, the prime mover in this artificial retreat, must remain confined therein. She lives and dies a prisoner, although her eggs can be wafted out on the currents of water, where they develop into free-swimming larvae.

There are creatures of the sea that are so highly adapted to their state of parasitism that they have lost all resemblance to their archetypal forms. The larva of *Sacculina* is typically crustacean, and swims freely in the sea until it is led by some impulse to attach itself to a part of a crab, often one of its legs. Here for a while it clings on to a hair by means of its antennules. Its subsequent behaviour is most extraordinary. The larva bores through the skin at the base of the hair, and when it has contacted the blood stream, the contents of its body quickly degenerate into a formless mass of cells, which pass into the interior of the crab. The shell of the larva is left clinging to the crab's leg, but soon falls off.

The mass of cells, which we may now regard as the embryo of the parasite, is carried about in the blood-stream of the crab until it comes in contact with the underside of the lower part of the intestine. Here it becomes attached; it grows, absorbing the juices of the crab, and at this stage sends out root-like structures into the crab's tissues. It travels along the intestine till it reaches the underside of the abdomen. Here it remains inside the crab until such time as the crab undergoes its next moult. After the moult, when the crab body is soft, a portion of the parasite protruudes externally in the form of a fleshy, sac-like mass on the underside of the abdomen.

This fleshy mass is far removed both in appearance and structure from that of the free-moving crustacean, and had it not been for the larval form no one would ever suspect any relationship.

The *Sacculina* now lives by means of the root-like branches which surround the intestine of the host. How this extraordinary ability to lose all of the typical organs of an arthropod, and to pass into the crab's body in a formless mass of cells, has been achieved by the *Sacculina* remains a mystery, which can only be compared with the strange breaking up of tissues which takes place during the metamorphosis in insects. The question presents itself: What is the governing principle which first breaks down one organism, and then guides the resulting formless mass to its appointed end of reproduction? The sac ultimately bursts, and lets loose thousands of eggs into the sea, which in turn develop into the free-swimming larval form; and so the life-cycle is completed. Can such a mysterious sequence of events be explained?

Another case of an extreme change of a parasitic form from that of a free living animal is offered by an allied genus called *Thompsonia*. This creature is found living parasitically on prawns and shrimps. Its external appearance consists of a number of small protruding sacs, sometimes as many as two hundred on a single host. When *Thompsonia* first came under observation it was assumed that each of these sacs was a separate parasite. It was later demonstrated that these sacs are all connected within the host with a central system that can be compared to the mycelium of a fungus: a thin thread, which is wound most thickly around the dorsal nerve cords of the host, and which sends branching threads down into the muscles. Lateral roots pass into the limbs and swimmerets, and it is on the ends of these that the external sacs are budded out. Within the sacs the ova grow, mature and undergo their whole development. The eggs develop into larvae while still within the membrane of the sac. When ready for a free existence, they burst, and the larvae, which are typically crustacean, escape into the sea.

This creature has almost forfeited its right to be called an animal. It is a mere thread, a mycelium, producing and nourishing a number of egg-bearing sacs. It has no senses, no organs save reproductive ones, and its affinities in the world of living things are only recognised through the larval form. It exists for mere life's sake, without hearing, sight, sense of smell or touch, and probably without even sensibility to pain. Degeneration could hardly go further; yet this creature follows always the same general manner of weaving its mycelium about the dorsal nervous system of its host. There is order which remains steadfast within fixed limits: the reproductive sacs are budded from the ends of the mycelium in crops, all appearing at the same time, synchronising with the shedding of the skin of the shrimp or prawn. If the larvae were not ready for the free-swimming stage, they would perish. In this fact there is intimation that the life rhythms of the host and parasite are in some unexplained way closely associated.

If we contrast the life in this creature that has degenerated from the archetypal form with the life in such a highly organised wasp as *Eumenes*, we see a vastly different picture, yet one that is no better or worse within its environment.

Among the fascinating stories of animal life told by the French naturalist Henri Fabre is that of the sand wasp *Eumenes*. The fertilised female builds a little domed house of sand spicules on some stone or rock foundation. The foundation ring is traced in minute pebbles. On this she builds a series of concentric rings, each diminishing in circumference, so as to enclose a domed space. At the top she leaves a hole. She then begins collecting certain species of small caterpillars. She stings these into a partial paralysis, but does not kill them, for they will be needed as fresh meat for the young she will never see.

When the wasp has collected either five or ten caterpillars, she prepares to close the dome, reducing the size of the hole. She now goes through a complicated process which would seem to indicate foresight on her part. Yet she has no foresight, only a highly developed instinct. From her ovipositor she excretes a juicy substance, working it with her legs into a narrow, inverted cone. With a thread of the same substance, she stitches the cone to the top of her domed building. Into the inverted cone, she lays an egg. She then seals up the hole, leaving the egg safe within the cone, suspended on a thread. This done, she goes off and builds another cone to repeat the same cycle of events.

In a short time the egg hatches into a tiny, white grub, so helpless and delicate that if placed among the still-living caterpillars on the floor of the dome, it would inevitably be injured. In its cradle it is safe. When hungry it spins a thin thread of its own, on which it descends and takes a bite of caterpillar. If the wriggling caterpillars appear threatening, it can retreat up the thread, and wait. In this way the grub spends its infancy; but, as it grows stronger, it risks a final descent, and devours, at its leisure, the still living food that mother has so satisfactorily provided.

From the domes that contain five caterpillars male wasps emerge; from where there are ten caterpillars, the larger female wasps. This raises an interesting question: Does the amount of food determine the sex? The mother wasp, who appears throughout her lifetime as a highly nervous and brilliantly alive creature, has built just the right sort of houses for the offspring she will never see; and has provided just the right amount of food. She is singularly well-adapted for her life; she stings the caterpillars just enough to keep them quiet, but not enough to kill them; she packs each dome with the right amount of food for male or female grub. The suspended cradle protects the tender infant from the rough reactions of the caterpillars while being eaten. Everything is in order, and as the emerging sand wasp dries her wings in the summer sunshine, she must surely feel that God is in his heaven, and all is well with the world. The caterpillars might harbour different sentiments.

This pattern seems to portray an unconscious and prophetic knowledge of events to come. It is as though she knew whether, when her building operations are complete, she will lay a male or female egg. The generally accepted belief is that the sex is already determined by the arrangement of genes in the fertilised egg. If this is so, the wasp must be controlled by an infallible guide within the unconscious workings of her body as to the sex of the egg she will be ready to lay when her dome is completed. Nature certainly propounds puzzles for any who would suggest premature answers.

Another such puzzle provided by the metamorphosis which takes place in the life cycle of insects is especially well developed in the lepidoptera. This complete form of metamorphosis may be taken as an illuminating expression of the transformative process of life, which may lead to a fuller understanding of the formative forces which govern the development of living things. The marked difference in form, size and habit which separate the early phases of the larva from the quiescent pupa, and from the final stage of the perfect insect cannot fail to evoke the question: How can the transformation from larva to pupa to imago be reconciled with the concept of *continuous* modifications by innumerable variations occurring over a great length of time, or with the concept of evolution by gradual functional changes? Further, how can the histolysis in the chrysalis, by which most of the organs are reduced to an emulsion, preparatory to the coming metamorphosis, be brought about by mechanistic physico-chemical actions? Here is a living testimony, which declares that neither the growth of the larva nor the mysterious breaking down of tissues in the chrysalis lead up to or anticipate the future form of the imago. They rather suggest an end-cause, a predetermined ideal, proper to, and working within, (and perhaps without) the organism; this ideal being the determining factor which governs the transformations.

The process can be observed in any butterfly or moth. I choose one that I have been able to observe both in the wild state and in confinement, feeding off a bunch of carrot leaves in my study. *Papilio machaon,* the swallowtail butterfly, still survives in Wicken Fen and other fens of Cambridgeshire. It is common on the Continent of Europe. Its life history may be taken as typical, and since it may give life to the picture, many details in the development are given in full. The eggs are laid on hog's fennel or wild carrot or wild angelica in the latter part of May and throughout June. The female does not usually lay more than one egg on any particular plant. When several caterpillars are found on the same plant they represent the layings of several butterflies. The eggs are bright yellow at first but turn brown as they grow older, and finally acquire a purple tinge. After about a week the young caterpillars eat their way out; their first meal is the egg-shell. They are black with a tiny white band; they sit near the end of a leaf frond, making no attempt to conceal themselves. In a few days they change their skins, or rather burst their way out of the skins with which they were first provided, and which are now too small for them. The new skin, which has been formed beneath the old one, looks on first emergence too large for the contained caterpillar; and so it is, for it is large enough to allow room for growth; when the caterpillar has grown so that this skin in turn is stretched to full capacity, it splits, and the larva emerges with yet another new skin, which has grown beneath the old one. At these skin-changes, the head, or rather the chitinous head-covering, is also shed. If the larva is observed just before the change, the old head can be seen sitting like a small hat upon the new larger head which is beneath.

At the time of change, the caterpillar will spin a small silk mat on which to fasten its claspers. Only when the claspers are firmly secured is the caterpillar able to walk out of the old skin, and leave it fastened to the mat. It is usually fatal to the larva to move it from its mat at the time of skin-changing, for if the hold is broken, and the caterpillar has entered into the quiescent stage which precedes the change, it is unable to walk clear of the old covering, which remains tightly about it, and it dies. For this reason, it is a good plan when collecting caterpillars never to move them from their food-plant, but to pick the spray on which they are feeding.

At each skin change the young swallowtail becomes more brightly marked. At the second change the white band is broader and has markings of orange and red. The fully-fed larva is very conspicuous in stripes of yellow-green and black, with red tubercles on the black bands. If it is alarmed it will bend the first few segments into an arch, and from between the second and third segment will produce pale orange emergences, which look like tentacles, and at the same time a drop of pungent liquid will be extruded. This probably serves to warn any ill-advised bird that this creature, with its brilliant colours, will afford an unpleasant-tasting mouthful.

Thirty days after the emergence from the egg the caterpillar is fully fed, and is ready for the change into the pupa stage. This readiness for change is announced by a restlessness and desire to walk. When kept in captivity, there is need for a hutch in which to confine these larvae; they will sit during the period of their growth peacefully on their food-plant; but at this later stage they will leave the food-plant, and, if not shut up, will be found going at a full gallop all over the room. This activity is not produced by want of food, nor is it primarily a search for a good place to pupate. It is engendered by an inner restlessness, and seems to be undertaken for the sake of mere walking. In some species, it is more marked than in the swallowtail. The larvae of the peacock butterfly will walk a great distance at this time, and many caterpillars show signs of being ill at ease, and have a definitely sickly appearance, indicating that the changes of their coming metamorphosis are already at work within them. Their colour changes, and a marked shrinkage of size is noticeable. This walking-sickness, as it may well be called, fulfils the purpose of distributing the individual larvae over wide areas, and in natural conditions they are scattered far from the place where the parent insect deposited the eggs. In gregarious caterpillars, such as those of the peacock and small tortoise-shell, this must be a definite help. In the breeding-cage, or in a room, the caterpillar will walk the destined number of yards, round and round, and up and down, and will then begin the important business of preparing for the change.

In the case of the swallowtail, the insects are now definitely smaller than when, fully fed, they began to walk, and of a yellower colour. The first act is to spin a firm thick mat on which to fix the hind claspers. This is usually made on the dry stalk of a reed or blade of sedge. In an upright position, with the hind claspers fixed to the mat, the larva spins the band which is to hold the pupa in position. This difficult task involves much neck-bending. From side to side the head goes, while the fore-feet guide and fasten the thread as far down the reed-stem as they can reach. The work is done slowly and with numerous rests. When it is completed, the caterpillar is circled round the back by a strong silk cord. It now rests facing the reed-stem, and with the legs drawn close up under the head. During this period of rest the body shrinks and becomes noticeably smaller, and towards the later part of the time, all the claspers but the last pair release their hold on the reed, and the creature leans on its band of silk in a shape already suggestive of the pupa it is about to become.

At the appointed time, usually after about fifty hours of quiescence, definite and rhythmical movements can be observed. These swell from the posterior to the anterior end, and announce the immediate change from larva to pupa. These swellings and contractings become increasingly marked, until they become sufficiently violent to break the thin larval skin, which splits down the back, when a green tender body pushes itself through the widening gap; at the same time, the skin, as though pulled back by some invisible instruments, slips farther and farther towards the posterior end. It passes, in a way which appears quite miraculous, the silk cord (which one would expect to entangle it) and by what can only be described as the most extraordinary dexterity of wriggling, the new naked pupa works the skin down to the region of the hind claspers. As a penultimate act, it releases its hold on the silk mat, draws up the tail (it is now supported only by the silk cord, which looks perilously like slipping) lifts clear of the skin, pushes the skin aside, and finally fastens again on the mat, giving as a seal of its accomplishment a few quick turns of the tail to make secure its hold.

The empty skin falls, and the pupa now occupies the place of the larva; but it has not yet assumed the final pupal form. The posterior end is much rounder than it will soon become, and the part where the eyes and the head are to be is still snub and soft. This condition changes within twenty minutes, the chrysalis takes its final shape, and the outer integument hardens.

The shape and position of the organs of the butterfly-to-be are already stamped on the pupa. It should be particularly noticed that these marks are on the *outside*, and that there is nothing yet formed inside to correspond with them. This is a significant fact, and one which, when its significance is grasped, will modify the accepted idea that development takes place chiefly from a centre outwards. The governing idea has at this stage declared itself, and although there is within the creature little else but a green watery pulp, all the places which are later to be occupied by legs, wings, antennae, etc., are now definitely marked on the chrysalis. They are waiting to be filled by organs not yet made, but pre-determined.

The changes which go on within are no less, and perhaps even more, wonderful than those which have been visible from the outside. A breaking down of the tissues is taking place, and has been taking place for some time. Cells which are comparable to white blood-corpuscles are generated in large numbers at this time, and these devour most of the organs which have functioned in the caterpillar, reducing them to a kind of soup. These changes within the chrysalis are not altogether known, and even in their physical aspect remain very much of a mystery; but it is maintained that the tissues which are reduced by the phagocytes comprise the hypodermic cells of the first four segments, the breathing tubes, the muscles, the fatty-bodies and the peripheral nerves, and of these there remain no cellular elements. They are reduced to a non-cellular mush. At the same time as this change is taking place, the cells of the middle intestine assemble into a central mass. Later a new generation of tissue is formed, partly from this central intestinal magma, and partly from the proliferation of special corpuscles called imago-bearing discs. Thus it is that the newly formed portions seem to have no direct affiliation with the destroyed parts of the larval organism. The creature has in fact died in so far as it has lost its form, its organs and its habits; and now, in a manner which cannot be described as anything but mysterious, it is experiencing a new orientation towards quite a different form, which is to find its expression in a quite different mode of life.

It may be maintained that this process of metamorphosis represents the working of a concrete idea upon a plastic material. The idea of what the future insect is to be impresses itself on a substance that has become non-structural and amorphous. If this statement is questioned, the questioner has but to look at the form impressed on the outer integument of the chrysalis *when as yet no organs are formed within it*. What we have witnessed is the workings of a directive force, which determines the chemical and physical reactions of the organic medium.

Although the changes that take place within the pupal case are in the present state of our knowledge to a large extent obscure, the emergence of the butterfly can easily be observed. Caterpillars which have been brought up in captivity can be induced to pupate on convenient reed-stems, and these, if kept out of the sun, usually produce butterflies the following June. Unfortunately I have never been able to observe the pupae in their native habitat, for although the larvae and ova are easy to find, the pupae are very difficult to see, as their colour, which is green or grey-black, blends perfectly with their surroundings. It would be interesting to know whether the pupa at this stage in its metamorphosis is acceptable to the palate of birds, and whether for this reason it is protectively coloured.

The emergence of the butterfly usually takes place between seven and eight in the morning. For some days previously the markings of the butterfly have been visible through the thin transparent shuck of the pupa. These markings, which on their first appearance are but faint, become darker daily until, on the last day the tone is mottled black and yellow, these being the predominant colourings of the emerged insect.

The first sign that a change is about to take place is an expanding of the thoracic region. This is at first rhythmical and barely to be marked, but it soon becomes more violent and spasmodic. Before long the pupa-shuck splits down the back and across the shoulders. The internal swellings and contractings become still more marked, though often relieved with intervals of rest, and soon the broad black back of the butterfly begins to push itself out and up; at the same time as this happens, the front of the pupa-case cracks in several places in the region of the legs and antennae. Soon the legs are thrust forth, the antennae are released and the trunk withdrawn from the sheath where it has lain. With an effort that now reaches its climax, the butterfly lifts itself, on its newly-freed legs, up on to the reed and draws the abdomen free of the case. Sometimes it will rest on the case itself, but more frequently on the reed. On its back are crumpled and misshapen masses, which are the wings; these are small, fleshy and thick, giving the creature, at this time, a crippled appearance.

As soon as the insect has found a firm standing-ground, at the correct angle, so that the wings can hang down over the back, it remains quite still except for a regular pumping movement, which is effected by a swelling and contracting of the thorax. By this movement the green sap-like blood is pumped into the nerves of the wings, and this gradually expands them. As the wings grow larger they fall limply over the back; should they now by any mischance become injured, the blood will well out of the wound, and the wing will not develop.

Invisible forces activate the visible phenomena of living things; Nature expresses invisible values in visible terms. To try to explain phenomena in terms of its appearance can never be satisfactory. More terms have to be put into our ideas before we can come near to any comprehension of facts. If we make the assumption that there is an invisible yet objective environment, conditioning the objects that our senses perceive, we can find many facts to support it. It has been called the spiritual world; its boundaries are undefined, and we know, as yet, little about it. We can discern only that the apparent evolution of forms can well be seen as a gradual incarnation. Extra senses may be necessary to gather extra knowledge; and who can say that they may not come into existence? Blake suggested that we should learn to look *through*, not only *with* our eyes. By this he meant that we gain what Goethe called "exact imaginative fantasy": the power to apprehend the noumenal that lies behind the phenomenal.

The tree of evolution and of life, as Darwin saw it, developed from the simple to the complex. On its branches there should have been found forms that connected the terminal twigs (the existing species) with the trunk from which they grew. The missing links are not to be found, either in extinct forms or otherwise; all are terminal twigs. But the tenuous substance that provides the connection remains in the invisible, which is, as yet, unmeasured, and are likely to remain unmeasured now that chemical sprays are exterminating our native fauna.

The vast body of this invisible tree, if it has being at all, is of some not-incarnate substance, a substance not yet descended into an incarnate state. This reverses the orthodox picture.

CHAPTER FOUR

THE CREATIVE WORD

Nature received the Word.

from the *Poemandres* of Hermes

At the end of its analysis physics is no longer sure what is left on its hands is pure energy or thought.

P. TEILHARD DE CHARDIN

" The Earth ", says the Greek author of the Sermons of Hermes, " first brought forth Man – bearing a fair gift, desiring to be mother, not of plants without feeling, nor brutes without reason, but a tamed God – loving life." This recognition of Man as archetype was general in the occult teachings of Egyptians, of Theraputes and neo-Platonists, and is found in many forms in religious doctrines, including Christianity. The Logos, the Virgin of the World, the Son of Man, Sophia and Maria Prophritissa are all symbolical expressions, denoting human attributes.

In the West this tradition has come down from pre-Christian times in the teachings of the mystery cults, the Alchemists and the Rosicrucians. It appears in the Mutabilie Cantos of Spenser's *Faerie Queen,* which are derived from the cabalistic speculations of the *Zohar*. Present day psychologists find in the souls of contemporary men thought-structures similar to ancient doctrinal patterns.

In recent times, these thoughts coincident with the ancient tradition have been revived and set forth with considerable detail in the works of Rudolf Steiner, who claims for his statement direct clairvoyant vision. The same – or much the same – ideas find a quasi-scientific form in the work of the Polish biologist, Dr Jaworski.

If we can be persuaded to consider this ancient doctrine in the light of modern biology, we meet an almost complete turning upside-down of orthodox ideas of evolution, as these have been taught in schools and colleges for the last eighty years. There are a few scientists who are uneasy about the modern theories, seeing that so many facts of plant and animal life are too complicated to be fitted into such comparatively simple frameworks. The ancient teaching claims to see in an aeon-long process of development, the evolution of men as a descent from the archetypal Man, or Logos. It postulates that men in becoming what they now are, have shed off from the original and potential (the Logos) plant and animal forms. These appear as what we are accustomed to look on as the evolutionary series. Each is a partial incarnation, a fragment, a symbol that expresses to our sense-perceptions a reality as yet unknown. This noumenal reality is termed by the psychologists, the unconscious; by men of religion it has been called God. To scientists it is the *Life*, which remains unknown in its essential essence. Each fragmentary expression, be it of plant, animal or mineral presents a partial aspect of the original; and since the original and potential cannot be divided in any absolute way, each fragmentary expression bears a noumenal, not yet incarnate, equivalent of its physical form.

The doctrine teaches that these incarnate fragments of the primal Logos have once been part of the archetypal Man, and have been shed off from him in the process of his development. They leave in men traces of equivalents of their essential plant and animal qualities. As man has changed, these forms have come into existence; they have become what Heinrich Steffens* has called "fixed ideas incarnate". In contrast to the animals, Man is not yet fixed as regards his development in consciousness, though seriously threatened by ideologies and by the risk of being enslaved by his adventure in technology.

To the man of letters or to the philosopher the idea of the archetypal Man is not so foreign as to the biologists. In English literature it has many advocates: Spenser, Milton, Blake and

* Note: Heinrich Steffens, German philosopher and scientist, 1773-1845.

Shelley; Emerson and Whitman in American; Goethe, Heine, Wagner and Nietzsche in German; Victor Hugo and Lamartine in French. The inspiration of these writers springs from the basic stem, though presenting divergent branches.

As Blake expresses it:

Man looks out in tree and herb and fish and bird and beast, collecting up the scattered portions of his immortal body into the elemental forms of everything that grows.
(*Vala.* VIII. 550-573)

Or as Edmund Spenser:

This great grandmother of all Creatures bred,
Great Nature, ever young, yet full of eld;
Still moving, yet unmoved from her sted;
Unseen of any, yet of all beheld.
(*Faerie Queene.* Mutability Cantos 7.13)

Or as Milton:

One first matter all,
Indu'd with various forms, various degrees
Of substance, and in things that live, of life;
The more refined, more spirituous, and pure,
As nearer to him placed or nearer tending. . . .

Flowers and their fruits,
Man's nourishment, by gradual scale sublim'd
To vital spirits aspire, to animal,
To intellectual. . . .
Differing but in degree, in kind the same.
(*Paradise Lost.* V. 473.)

To Milton the fall of man involved the animals, they becoming mortal as he had done.

And Whitman speaking of the reality that is behind appearance:

The Mystery of Physical Life

I hear and behold God in every object, yet understand God not in the least.

Goethe speaks of this unknown as "The Mothers";

Um sie kein Ort, noch weniger eine Zeit;
Von ihnen sprechen ist Verlegenheit.
Die Mütter sind es.

(*Faust*. Part II 1600-1680.)

In other places Goethe speaks of "exact imaginative fantasy", which can discern qualities in the object that correspond to qualities within the observer. Swedenborg has something of the same idea, so also Gustav Fechner. Another variant is found in Browning's poem *Paracelsus*. He attributes to Paracelsus the idea that "the scattered attributes of Man strewed confusedly about inferior natures, all lead up higher to shape out dimly a superior race."

The Hindu scientist and Nobel Prizewinner, Sir Jagadir Chandra Bose, has sought to prove the existence of a constant property of life in matter, organic and inorganic. He shows that minerals can be made tired, can be poisoned and made ill, and treated for their sickness. He chloroformed vegetables and restored them to normal life. All things in nature share with men one quality in common, though varying greatly in degree.

In man, consciousness develops from the unconsciousness (or apparent unconsciousness) of a young child to normal self-consciousness; it can go further into exact, imaginative perception, and into clairvoyant vision. In a subsequent chapter it will be shown that clairvoyant consciousness was of commoner occurrence in earlier times than amongst men of today. In past times when science, philosophy and religion were, for the generality of mankind, contained within a diffuse apprehension of life, men relied on their sense of wonder, rather than on exact measurement and ratiocination, to help interpret the riddle of the universe. To-day it is within our power to wonder with deeper penetration, since our knowledge of form and function is more exact. We know more about our bodies and the processes of metabolism. It would seem that the next step is to relate the inner activities of our morphological and physiological make-up to the outer universe, finding (what the ancient sages saw to be) correspondence in the outer world. Modern psychology is engaged in this task, and Dr Jung has stated in more places than one, that a man draws towards him those outward events which his inner orientation demands; his destiny and his view of outward events is determined by his state of awareness.

Coincident with our outward and conscious experience are dimly-perceived undercurrents, which are partly revealed in dreams. These balance our outward adventures, and should we scrutinise them they can be made conscious, thus adding to our understanding. In contrast to such understanding, modern science, so markedly distinguished for knowledge of technology and impulsion towards adventures into outer space, is correspondingly unconcerned with adventures into the vast unexplored regions of introspection. Only with reluctance is psychology accepted as a borderline science, and that but recently. The philosophers and seers of the ancient world concentrated on inner life, realising that the outer world exists as such only in so far as it is consciously reflected, and consciously expressed by the soul. They became aware of the truth that consciousness is a pre-condition of being. The soul as the bearer of consciousness is co-evolved with the principle of physical being. In their own field they entered regions that extended beyond the experience of most men. Their adventures in the inner realms were certainties, as firm as modern mechanics are for contemporary bridge-builders.

In *Poemandres* of Hermes are intuitive apprehensions about the true place of man in the universe. In one of the dialogues between Hermes and the universal Mind we find the following:

"Now things lie in one way in the bodiless, another way in being made manifest.

"Think then of Him who doth contain them all; and think, that than the bodiless naught is more comprehensive, or swifter, or more potent, but that it is the most comprehensive, the swiftest and most potent of them all.

"And thus think from thyself, and bid thy soul go into any land; and there more quickly than thy bidding will it be. And bid it journey oceanwards; and there again immediately it will be, not as passing on from place to place, but as being there.

"And bid it mount to heaven; and it will need no wings, nor aught will hinder it, nor fire of sun, nor aether, nor vortex-swirl, nor bodies of the other stars; but cutting through them all, it will soar up to the last body of them all. And shouldest thou will to break through this as well, and contemplate what is beyond – if there be aught beyond the Cosmos – it is permitted thee.

"Behold what power, what swiftness, thou dost have! And canst thou do all of these things, and God not do them?

"Then in this way know God; as having all things in Himself as thoughts, the whole Cosmos itself.

"If thou doest not make thyself like unto God, thou canst not know Him. For like is knowable to like alone. Make thyself grow to the same stature as the Greatness which transcends all measures; leap forth from every body; transcend all Time, become Eternity: and thus shalt thou know God.

"Conceive nothing is impossible unto thyself, think thyself deathless and able to know all – all arts, sciences the way of every life. Become more lofty than all height, and lower than all depth. Collect unto thyself all senses of all creatures – of fire, and water, dry and moist. Think that thou art at the same time in every place – in earth, in sea, in sky; not yet begotten, in the womb, young and all, and dead, in after-death conditions. And if thou knowest all these things at once – times, places, doings, qualities and quantities, thou canst know God.

"But if thou lockest up thy soul within thy body, and dost debase it, saying; I nothing know; I nothing can: I fear the sea; I cannot scale the sky; I know not who I was, who shall be – what is there then between thy God and thee?

Hermes asks: —

"Is God unseen? And Mind answers: "Hush! Who is more manifest than He? For this one reason He hath made all things, that through them thou mayest see Him . . . Mind sees itself in thinking, God in making."

A vision so superlative may seem far from the insignificant lives of such creatures as sea-slugs and fig wasps, but should there be no link between the perception of small things and intuitive apprehension of the cosmos, the vision would be void, and patterns of life without meaning. What we perceive with the senses is not unrelated to the insight of poet or seer, nor are things of smaller graces unrelated to greater glories.

The method of modern science is to relate the forms and functioning of living creatures, to classify and compare, and to rule out as far as possible subjective interpretations, forgetting that the perceptions of the human psyche are co-evolved with physical being. The one must effect the other; one might say that the one created the other. Close and continuous scrutiny of living organisms affects organisms, and organisms affect human beings, however unconscious either party may be. According to the wave-length to which we are tuned, so we change. Dr Jung tells a story of a man who thought it amusing to kill toads by looking at them in a malignant way. He found he could do it, but one day a toad looked back at him and he became partially paralysed. He came to the doctor to be cured.

When we rule out the awareness of this reciprocal relation we make of men mere spectators; but since we ourselves are *in life,* it is impossible to separate ourselves from the changing conditions that constitute life. Without observation we know nothing. All things exist within the range of our perceptions. They may appear as hopelessly perplexing enigmas, or as symbols of a reality as yet unknown. Goethe, who had looked deeper into Nature than most men, saw all material things as symbols. By our perception we awaken a quality which simultaneously flashes into significance in the object and in ourselves: the quality which perceives. The correspondence between the object and ourselves is "of its own birth, the life and element".* With wonder comes the awareness of the creative impulse hidden in Nature. This is not obvious to casual inspection, nor to exact measurement; it remains as a light that is darkened. "The Light shineth in darkness and the darkness comprehendeth it not." If we take the light to mean consciousness, and it can mean nothing else, then our own awareness does indeed recognise the essential light of creation hidden in Nature. It needs not only our scrutiny, but also something awakening in ourselves to comprehend the creative power: the light of the Logos, the primal impulse.

How may this light be awakened?

By increasing consciousness that leads to clairvoyant vision. It suffices to say that as consciousness expands, so outer perceptions deepen, and we may come to see ourselves as no mere cyphers in an endless alphabet of existence, but, as Dr Watts expressed it:

Were I so tall to reach the pole
Or grasp the ocean with a span,
I must be measured by my soul:
The mind's the standard of the man.

* Coleridge. "Ode to Dejection."

Which surely means that those with larger consciousness will comprehend more of the light that shineth in the darkness. The history of the evolution of human thought is the discovery of the meaning that hides within its obscurity, the obscurity which confronts us with so many contradictions.

The most puzzling of enigmas is that the creative impulse itself presents obstructions.

This obstruction within the overall constitution of the human soul demands a special effort if it is to be overcome. How may we realise this enigma, this harshness, that would reap where no seed is sown? We hear with only one ear, the other being closed against the perplexities of the divine ethos. More is demanded than worship or belief: a transformation as of a gray-drake mayfly from the green-drake, a second emergence.

The classification of earthly things according to their qualities, already outlined in the second chapter, is as old as the Vedas; an idea generally adopted in ancient philosophies, and one that would seem to be a spontaneous expression, springing direct from the fount of life, and not in contradiction to the containing principle of a gradual incarnation of man as outcome of a descending spirit. Man, as we know him in the present stage of evolution has, besides his physical body, the invisible essence of life, complexes of desires, and, in addition, the Ego-principle, which can separate itself from objects, and can memorise. The higher animals which incarnated earlier have all that man has, but lack the Ego-Principle. Plants have the life and the physical body, the life of desire and cognition, remaining disincarnate in the spiritual world. The minerals have only the physical body. According to such classification all things are part-expression of the original impulse.

If such ideas seem arbitrary to our accustomed spectator's viewpoint, we have the means to put them to the test: to look deeper, to look as Hermes was bidden in his conversation with the Universal Mind.

The ingenious faculties which have invented radio and television should be capable, if attention is turned in that direction, to tuning-in directly to the life-principle, let us say, of a tree-frog, or a herd of red deer (as Fraser Darling has done), or to the life-vibrations of microscopic organisms when watched under a cover-slip (as H. S. Jennings has done). We should not fall short of capacity. Such a tuning-in would lead to conscious and controlled participation with the objects of our regard. In them we find each life pulsating to an ordered rhythm, in ordained and Gestalt patterns, which only through chance can find a change. Such patterns are found in plant and animal behaviour; they seem to be conditioned by chance. Darwin saw evolution as the product of chance variations, and this, if taken in the larger aspect, is a true finding; yet too simple, if chance is not approached in its deeper aspect.

To scrutinise the workings of chance is to come near to the workings of a mystery, for at the moment in which any one particular thing happens, we touch the presence of life itself. The ancient Chinese wisdom of the *I Ching*, the Book of Changes, has in Wilhelm's commentary the following passage:

"Suprahuman intelligence has from the beginning made use of three mediums of expression – men, animals, and plants, in each of which life pulsates in different rhythms. Chance came to be utilised as a fourth medium; *the very absence of an immediate meaning in chance permitted a deeper meaning to come to expression in it.*"

Into the empty-seeming vacuum of chance, we look to gather significance; and the astonishing thing is that significance can be found in the relation between the gestalt patterns offered by Nature and our own subjective tuning-in. By persistent application and devoted scrutiny over indefinite periods of time, a single moment may become illuminated, an intuitive flash, a vision, a looking-through; it can lead to a subjective change in the observer, such as William Blake experienced when he said that he could look at a knot in a piece of wood till he was frightened at it. Looking at the knot, he participated in the life of the tree, the growing-point that had thrust out the lateral branch; all the mysterious activities of life and growth and becoming, and death, all are present in a moment of perception. Such an experience reaches out to find behind the appearance of the observed object a significance of which the object is an ever-growing, ever-changing, ever-disappearing symbol. In such experience the changing, *changeful* moment affords a link between the observer and the object. Within this changefulness resides a freedom from the accustomed sequence of events, in so far as they become simultaneous, and a deeper meaning is in part revealed. We may think of such happenings when they come to us, sometimes with shattering unexpectedness, as destiny, or, in the language of Indian philosophy, as *karma*, or as the will of the gods, or the workings of the Holy Ghost, or, in more prosaic language, as the power of the unconscious, always latent, but now active.

Poets in their moods of penetration perceive suprahuman intelligence. All great poets move in a world of faerie, peopled by unsubstantial beings. Shakespeare, Milton, Spenser, Shelley, Keats, afford examples, and Rilke speaking in our own time of his penetration into the region of the moment:

Here come too, fully conscious,
Many creatures, many sure-footed mountain beasts,
Pausing and passing, and the great bird dwelling in secret
Soars round the pure and forbidding summits no longer
Secret, here on the high hills of the heart.

In this way men become aware of realities beyond the physical life, as revealed through human sensibilities, and they grow more sensitive in ever-expanding apprehension. Primitive men in past ages conceived of their gods in subjective imaginations that enfolded outward events just so far as their capacities allowed; the inner situation finding itself in outer symbols, and then, gradually, in one experience and another. As they changed, they bound them to the image of their own making and in their own gesture, until, changing further, and entering deeper into the meaning of their earthly life, they vaguely apprehended the reality of the pre-existing Logos that embraced all things with an overpowering persuasiveness, as the incarnating and evolutionary principle of life.

Life, in all manifestations, provides symbols of interpretation, in each a fragment of the whole, a focal centre through which may be discerned the nouminal reality, without which there is no satisfying interpretation of living things. Such an affirmation, taken as a working hypothesis, may be found more adequate to cover observed facts and theories, into which so many facts refuse at present to be fitted.

We seek insight into the relationships of plant and animal. The patterns of life are gestalt patterns that would seem, at first observation, firmly set in their peculiar and various forms. The quality of our understanding of these, together with their assignments of cause and effect, are subjective, and change with the consciousness of the observer. They may lie dormant, or may be half awake. A man's *immediate* sense of awareness does not always arouse them. The element of Chance has been thought of by Chinese sages to contain that apparent nothingness in which the gods are free to move and influence the three mediums of expression – men, animals and plants. This is not at variance with the idea of Karma, which postulates an invisible and determinant power, manifesting from incarnation in incarnation; nor does it in any way contradict the overall picture of the archetypal Man (Logos) in descent into incarnation from a suprasensible.

With such thoughts in mind we are in a position to look more closely at some of the patterns of plant and animal behaviour, and ask how they can be reconciled with an overall picture of the gradual descent into incarnation of a Creative

Impulse from out of the region of the suprasensible. To such patterns it may be possible to tune-in; to obtain, if not yet a clear and definite image, some suggestion of a bridge between the subjective apprehension of the observer and the Creative Thought that gives rise to all objects.

CHAPTER FIVE

ACTIVE PARTICIPATION

The Christian symbol is a living thing that carries in itself the needs of further development. It can go on developing; it depends only on us, whether we can make up our minds to meditate again more thoroughly, on the Christian premises. This requires a very different attitude towards the individual, towards the microcosm of the self, from the one we have had hitherto. That is why nobody knows what ways of approach are open to man, what inner experience he can still pass through and what psychic facts underlie the religious myth.

C. G. Jung

If mythology represents an attempt to express and articulate the truths of religion, religious experience itself issues from living in direct contact with the ultimate mystery.

N. Berdyaev

There is a saying by Alexander Hertzen, himself an idealist and a dreamer, that has in it a dangerous truth; "You can only work on men's minds by dreaming their dreams more clearly than they can dream them themselves, not by demonstrating their ideas to them as geometrical theorems are demonstrated." This implies that if men are to respond to outward suggestion, entrance must be made to the unconscious background where thinking begins, to that region where conscious thought mingles with the unconscious springs of being. To elaborate his meaning, we may say that the conscious will of him who would work on man must enter into the unconscious of those who are to be worked on. When we apply this thought to our own experience, when we ourselves are to be worked on by ourselves, then this saying has value and truth. We must enter with consciousness into our own dreaming. In entering into this "dreamland" of thought there is danger – unless effort is made by the conscious mind to remain conscious: to dream collective dreams, as Hitler did, may be the most disastrous of human activities. The only thought that really moves ourselves, or any other men, is that which springs new-made in the mind, for men are not deeply convinced by the demonstration of geometrical theorems. Conviction comes as a light shining in darkness, which, in its own light, is aware of the darkness. Illumination comes when attention is awakened to a feeling of participation with outer objects. An element of awareness flows from the observer to find recognition in the thought embodied in the object. This spark of kindling awareness can bring about (and reside in) a mingling of the observing subject and the observed object. It is accompanied by a feeling of exultation, and it often leads those who experience such a mingling to a greater intensity of life; or it can more easily lead them into a state of disintegration and death. If the spark burns clear in consciousness it leads to life; if it merges back into the unconsciousness of mass movements it leads to destruction. It is this spark which has been thought of as the Christ Spirit, of which the author of the Logoi wrote: "In all things I am scattered, and whenever thou willest thou gatherest Me, and gathering Me, gathereth thyself."* The experience of such relation between the observing subject and the object is an *individual* experience, illuminating the object in an individual way, and lifting it above the general psychic average of recognition. In our usual state we see a knot in a piece of wood, but Blake, with his greater intuitive apprehension, saw more than is ordinarily seen. He looked, as he said, not only *with* his eyes, but *through* them. In something of the same way a specialist who concentrates attention on some particular animal or plant sees qualities that shine forth into being as he himself calls them forth.

In earlier chapters descriptions of animal and plant be-

* *Oxyrhynchus Logio.* Granville and Hunt.

haviour have been outlined in exact detail. In this chapter experiences of individual observers of illumination and recognition, are cited.

Over the oceans of the world, cruising from polar regions, north and south, still sports, though cruelly hunted, that great leviathan, the sperm whale. He is remarkable for his huge size, from eighty to ninety feet long when mature. The full circumference at the widest is forty feet, the living weight at least ninety tons. Calculating the weight of thirteen men to be one ton, then the combined population of a village of eleven hundred inhabitants would be equal to the weight of one whale. Only in the vast spaces of great oceans could such a creature exist. Whether whales are highly intelligent we do not yet know, but it is certain that they have large and highly convoluted brains; brains far larger than a man's, and with as elaborate convolutions. Judging from the brain alone we are led to suppose that the whale has great potentialities of intelligence. Unlike man it cannot record its experience; there are no books for young whales to read. By each generation everything that can be learnt has to be learnt. Amongst the many monsters of the deep, it is probably the most highly conscious: an air-breathing mammal that has taken the ocean to be its breeding ground, its nursery, its wedding garment and its shroud.

Herman Melville's *Moby Dick*, that great epic of the sea, has for its dominating character a white whale of prodigious size and cunning, a symbol of unconscious forces being incarnated in one of the largest mammals, denizen of the vast ocean. Melville constructs his story on two levels: the inner life of man and an epic of the sea. The two sides exist independently but constantly converge; and as the author's inner discoveries flash into awareness, so outer events live with mysterious and majestic splendour.

On each soft side – coincident with the parted swell that but once leaving him, then flowed so wide away – on each bright side, the whale shed off enticings . . . and thus through the serene tranquilities of the tropical sea, among waves whose hand clappings were suspended by exciting rapture, Moby Dick moved on, still withholding from sight the full terror of his submerged trunk, entirely hiding the wretched hideousness of his jaw [such a description is not merely that of a living animal, but a realisation of "the grand god" that reveals himself, "then plunges down to deepest ocean depths."]. . . .

Hoveringly halting, and dipping on the wing, the white sea-fowls [appropriate symbols of human thoughts] longingly lingered over the agitated pool that he left.

Throughout this book the inner man reaches out to find himself in the ocean with its numerous denizens; in particular, the whale, where the human and the unknown meet. Of the breathing of the whale, Melville writes: "Man's one breath serves but one or two pulsations. But the sperm whale breathes about the seventh, or Sunday of his time". And of the spoutings, he writes:

And how nobly it raises our conceit of the mighty, misty monster, to behold him solemnly sailing through a calm tropical sea; his vast mild head overhung by a canopy of vapour – as you will sometimes see it – glorified by a rainbow, as if Heaven itself had put a seal upon his thoughts. For d'ye see, rainbows do not visit the clear air; they only irradiate vapour. And so, through all the thick mist of the dim doubts in my mind, divine intuitions now and then shoot, enkindling my fog with Heavenly ray. And for this, I thank God; for all have doubts or denials, a few among them have intuitions. Doubts of all things earthly, and intuitions of some things heavenly; this combination makes neither believer nor infidel, but makes a man who regards them both with equal eye."

Melville's most telling lines are those where he sees Nature in human form. "The pensive air was transparently pure and soft, with a woman's look, and the robust and man-like sea heaved with long, strong, lingering swells, as Samson's chest in his sleep." And again: "The strong, troubled, murderous thinkings of the masculine sea." And, under the surface, he describes the cannibal ways of sharks, sword fish and chimeras.

Deeper still, in the deepest depths where no light penetrates, in utter darkness, there is yet life in the monotonous cold under enormous pressure: certain small fish have adapted themselves to these extremities. Into depths, as yet fragmentarily explored, dredges have been lowered, deposits from the cold darkness have been brought up, fishes of peculiar shapes raised slowly, so that they may not be burst by the decreasing pressure.

Through the upper surface of the ocean light can penetrate to about a hundred and fifty fathoms; beyond this depth only animal life is fond. The creatures that live so far down subsist on the continuous rain of dead and dying organisms falling from lesser depths, and on each other. The sea floor is red dusty mud and littered with comparatively few skeletons of radiolaria and with the otoliths of whales. Calcareous skeletons, continually falling from above, have been dissolved by the pressure of overhead waters. At various depths of this hypobenthos, the pressure on living creatures varies from a ton to five tons to the square inch.

Despite complete darkness, monotonous cold and enormous weight of waters some small fishes have become adapted to the great deeps; creatures of horrific appearance, seeming to the human glance as though made of ill-fitting parts, joined together by hazard. Some of these dwellers in the darkness have phosphorescent organs or patches that give light. One, *Platocorynus spinicarpa,* carries a nose-lamp like the headlight of a motor car; another has a luminous lure on a flexible rod, raised and deflected, as enticement to smaller fishes, which are thus attracted into the jagged-toothed mouth: the gaping cavern of Hell as depicted by Hieronymous Bosch. Others are blind; some have enormous eyes, emitting a faint luminosity.

In this world, a male fish finds it difficult to locate his mate, since few exist under such conditions. Once found he does not lose her, uniting with her substance, sucking her juices for nourishment: an adhesion, finding a counterpart in no few human associations: a mere parasite, losing all functional activities save that of sperm-making. At the season when she casts her eggs into the sea, he squirts his sperm.

At the Natural History Museum of South Kensington there are dried specimens of such fish, and numerous prints and drawings to give food for imaginations: enormous, gaping mouths, unwinking eyes of unflinching purpose – original myths of creation – Tiamat and her brood; the deep dreams of the mentally deranged, frightful visages, endowed with powerful and irrational determination, fixed ideas incarnate in deep waters, dreams of Bosch and Breughel. The weight of oceans has "precipitated" their startled, indignant and suffering faces. In sex alone, a dim luminosity in the darkness.

Melville's aptitude for conscious participation illumines all his chronicled adventures. When he was a young man serving on an American man of war, he fell from high on a mast-head and was dragged down into deep water by his heavy and porous jacket. When he recovered consciousness from the fall he was already deep down, but retained enough life to wriggle out of the jacket. He rose swiftly, like Lazarus from the tomb, as a new man, having tasted of death, in his initiation. From then on he saw and felt in a new way. On his visit to the Encantadas Islands he tells, as did Darwin, of the huge land tortoises, and how his shipmates brought some of them on board ship.

> Ropes were dropped over, and presently three huge antediluvian looking tortoises, after much straining, were landed on deck. They seemed hardly the seed of earth . . . these

mystic creatures suddenly translated by night from uniterable solitudes to our peopled deck, affected me in a manner not easy to unfold . . . The greatest feeling inspired by these creatures was that of age, dateless, infinite endurance . . . Consider the impregnable armour of their living mail. What other living being possesses such a citadel wherein to resist the results of time?

As lantern in hand, I scraped among the moss and beheld the ancient scars of bruises received in many a sudden fall among the marly mountains of the isle–scars strangely widened, swollen, half-obliterated, and yet distorted, I seemed an antiquary of a geologist, studying the ciphers upon the slates trod by creatures whose very ghosts are now defunct.

As I lay in my hammock that night, I heard the slow, weary draggings of three ponderous strangers along the encumbered deck. Their stupidity or their resolution was so great, that they never went aside for any impediment. One ceased his movements altogether just before mid-watch. At sunrise I found him butted like a battering-ram against the immoveable foot of the foremast, and still striving, tooth and nail, to force the impossible passage. That these tortoises are the victims of a penal, or malignant, or downright diabolical enchanter, seems in nothing more likely than in that strange infatuation of hopeless toil which so often possesses them. I have known them in their journeyings ram themselves heroically against rocks, and long abide there, nudging, wriggling, wedging, in order to displace them, and so hold on their inflexible path. Their crowning curse in their drudging impulse to straightforwardness in a belittered world.

No need to stress the latent human qualities here revealed; a recognition and, in part, an enlightenment, for Melville often drew back as though frightened at his own understanding. He looked more closely at those tortoises than any of his shipmates, attributing to them their cosmic and human association. One peculiarity of the tortoise he does not mention. The tortoise has its pectoral girdle *inside* its ribs. All other vertebrates have the scapular outside the ribs. When we come to consider what a number of adjustments must be made for so large a variation from the normal, it is hard to think that all these, synchronising together to the end-plan of a tortoise, could have come together by chance.

If we think of the tortoises as descended from an ancestral reptile that followed the arrangement common to all other vertebrates possessing ribs, it is hard to imagine how the scapula got from outside the ribs to its position inside the ribs. It must be either outside or inside, there is no intermediate position. One might call this large step a mutation, carrying with it many other synchronising mutations in muscles and ligaments; but so large a mutation as that might just as well be called a creation, and if the scientific mind is frightened at the word, then call it precipitation. Precipitation it seems to be, since no other class of reptiles approach their peculiarities of form and habit. Turtles are of course like tortoises, but turtles are by general consent thought of as a devolution from the archetypal tortoise. The ancients thought of the tortoise as being so remote from the general order as to imagine the first tortoise to be a rebellious nymph who refused to be present at the nuptials of Zeus and Hera, and as punishment was turned into so curious and eccentric a form.

In many ways hunters and jungle-dwellers participate actively with the wild creatures that they know so well. Jim Corbett in his wonderful stories of tigers, leopards and jungle life has tuned his receiving-set to great sensibility. He recounts many occasions when he was hunting man-eating tigers and was aware of the hidden presence of the tiger waiting to pounce on him. The tiger also, without doubt, was well tuned to Jim Corbett; they had a true recognition in the life and death struggle. The tiger element in the hunter has roused itself to acute responsiveness to the beast that he is hunting. Unless he has cultivated an attitude quite devoid of vindictiveness, but with sympathy to the killer that he must kill, he could not have been the superb hunter that he was. In all his adventures he arouses his latent qualities to correspond with all that is mysterious and unknown to other men. Well might he say: "The Indian Jungle, which is a mystery to other men, has like a woman given me its joy." And continue the quotation from Scawen Blunt: "Time is my conquest, I can bear to die." Because fear so seldom enters his heart, he is the master of events.

In like manner, though not with such deeply graven assurance, J. H. Williams has entered into the lives of the elephant teams he worked with in the jungles of Northern Burma. Another naturalist with superb capacity for participation with the wilds of unexplored forest is Charles Waterton: may he never be forgotten! This eccentric and courageous explorer ventured alone into the jungles of South America. Unlike so many other explorers of strange lands he went with only the lightest equipment, and barefoot. He thus describes the few precautions he took against yellow fever, malaria and other ailments. "Shouldest thou ever wander through these remote and dreary wilds, forget not to carry with thee bark, laudanum, calomel and jalap, and lancet. There are no druggist shops here, nor sons of Galen to apply to in times of need. A thin flannel waistcoat under a check shirt, a pair of trousers, and a hat, were all my wardrobe; shoes and stockings I seldom had on. In dry weather they would have irritated the feet, and retarded me in the chase of wild beasts." Reading his book, rich in adventure, and full of sympathetic observation of all wild creatures, no reader can doubt that this man was able naturally to call on qualities in himself that were correspondent to the life impulses of snakes, frogs, lizards, sloths, jaguars, caymans, and, indeed, every kind of animal or bird or insect that inhabited those vast and wild forests that he observed so closely in every detail. By all ordinary standards he was an odd freak of a man, but a true naturalist; one who demonstrated that like is only known by like; we perceive only that which we are capable of perceiving. In describing the towering mora trees his perceptions are alert to the rhythmic beats of death and life, the one growing from and supplanting the other.

> The wild fig tree, as large as a common English apple tree, often rears itself from one of the thick branches at the top of the mora; and when its fruit is ripe, to it the birds resort for nourishment. It was to an undigested seed that the fig tree first owed its elevation there. The sap of mora raised it to full bearing, but now, in its turn, it is doomed to contribute a portion of its own sap and juices towards the growth of various species of vines, the seeds of which, also, the birds deposit on its branches. These soon vegetate, and bear fruit in great quantities; so that with their usurpation of the resources of the fig tree, and the fig tree of the mora, the mora, unable to support a charge which nature never intended it should, languishes and dies under its burden; and then the fig tree, and its usurping progeny of vines, receiving no more succour from their late foster-parent, droop and perish in their turn.

Another naturalist who enters with exceptional sympathy into the life of the creatures of his study is F. Fraser Darling, who also went barefoot when stalking the red deer in the forests of Dundonnell, Gruidard and Letterewe in Western Ross-shire. Knowing the roughness of the country he started with windproof clothing and climbing boots, but found he could not get near the deer. He took a kilt and abandoned boots and socks. After an anguishing time in hardening his feet he went barefoot with better success. After two years of close and conscious participation, he tuned in sufficiently to make himself so deer-like in vibrations that he was unnoticed in their midst.

On November 5th 1934, the weather was dead calm and cloudless above a good layer of snow. Just before dusk the temperature was 30 degrees, Fahr. and I was about to walk up Glen Chacrachain to watch the carn deer which were down on the quartzite slabs. I did not get within seventy yards of the burn, for the deer were coming through the birch trees and over the water. I stood against the trunk of a birch, motionless. The deer had not seen me and they came slowly on, browsing on tufts of bents and heather which showed through the snow. The light was falling, but the snow and the clear air helped to keep objects sharply visible. Three hinds and a stag approached the trees under which I stood. They rose on their hind legs and browsed on the twigs of the very one above me. I could have touched them, and their breath came in my face. Many more of the herd were within five to twenty yards. I had the feeling of having reached that state which all watchers of animals desire, of having dispensed with my physical presence. The deer moved on their grazing in twos and threes, and I was left alone under my tree in the still and silent air. They seem to have been unaware of me only three feet away from them.

Karen Blixen, whose genius was as of life itself, was naturally conditioned to find the bodiless made manifest in outward events; she has the rare power to see and to find in external events the sign of her condition. She tells in her book *Out of Africa* the story of her farm and of her friendships, and of how at the sudden death of a friend, coincident with the financial failure of the farm into which she had put so much and from which she had taken full recompense, she asked for a sign.

All this could not be, I thought, just a coincidence of circumstance, what people call a run of bad luck, but there must be some principle within it. If I could find it, it would save me. If I looked in the right place, I reflected, the coherence of things might become clear to me. I must, I thought, get up and look for a sign.

Many people think it an unreasonable thing, to be looking for a sign. This is because of the fact that it takes a particular state of mind to be able to do so, and not many people have found themselves in such a state. If, in this mood, you ask for a sign, the answer cannot fail you; it follows as the natural consequence of the demand. In the same way an inspired card-player collects thirteen cards on the table, and takes up what is called – a hand of cards – a unity. Where others see no call at all, he sees a grand slam staring him in the face. Is there a grand slam in the cards? Yes, to the right player.

I came out of the house looking for a sign, and wandered at haphazard towards the boys' huts. They had just let out their chickens, which were running here and there amongst the houses. I stood for a little while and looked at them.

Fathima's big white cock came strutting up before me. Suddenly he stopped, laid his head first on one side, and then on the other, and raised his comb. From the other side of the path, came a little grey Chameleon that was, like the cock himself, out on his morning reconnoitring. The cock walked straight upon it – for the chickens eat these things – and gave out a few clucks of satisfaction. The Chameleon stopped up dead at the sight of the cock. He was frightened, but he was at the same time very brave, he planted his feet in the ground, opened his mouth as wide as he possibly could, and, to scare his enemy, in a flash he shot out his club-shaped tongue, at the cock. The cock stood for a second as if taken aback, then swiftly and determinately he struck down his head like a hammer and plucked out the Chameleon's tongue.

The whole meeting between the two had taken ten seconds. Now I chased off Fathima's cock, took up a big stone and killed the Chameleon, for he could not live without his tongue; the Chameleons catch the insects that they feed on with their tongues.

I was so frightened by what I had seen – for it had been a gruesome and formidable thing in a miniature format – that I went away and sat down on the stone seat by the house. I sat there for a long time and Farah brought me out my tea, and put it on the table. I looked down on the stones and dared not look up, such a dangerous place did the world seem to me.

Very slowly only, in the course of the next few days, it came upon me that I had had the most spiritual answer possible to my call. I had even been in a strange manner honoured and distinguished. The powers to which I had cried had stood on my dignity more than I had done myself, and what other answer could they then give? This was clearly not the hour for coddling, and they had chosen to connive at my invocation of it. Great powers had laughed at me, with an echo from the hills to follow the laughter, they had said among the trumpets, among the cocks and Chameleons, Ha ha!

I was so pleased that I had been out this morning in time to save the Chameleon from a slow, painful death.

Hardy, whose great distinction was his capacity to enter with tenderness into the lives of living things, gave many instances in prose and poetry of sympathetic and conscious participation, and thus it is with all the great artists – and in particular with W. H. Hudson, the greatest of modern naturalists, who knew the English countryside as it was fifty years ago, when there still existed a plenitude of animal life; birds that are now never seen, birds that were then common and are now rare, butterflies that made beautiful and gay the woodland and downside, now nearly all poisoned by chemical sprays and fertilisers. Reading his books one finds an England that is past, where forests existed untraversed by motor highways, where birds and insects, living their natural lives, could find, in the perceiving eyes of men, their counterparts. "He wrote like the grass grows," Joseph Conrad said of him; and not only of England but of South Africa, where he spent his youth and boyhood.

In the dark forest bordering the upper reaches of the Orinoco river, within this secret heart of Nature, where few white men had at this time ventured, he set the idyll of a truly-conceived, imaginary adventure. The story is told as of a re-counted record, removing it from the obvious or personal, and so making it possible to have been an intimate, individual experience. Here Hudson, in his true nature of naturalist, poet and seer meets with a bird-like being, which is for him the *Anima Mundi*, the strange half-human, half divine Rima, who dazzles, bewilders and enchants him. The Green Mansions in which she lives are in the near neighbourhood of villages of degenerate natives. She is a creature of the forest and the forest trees; the friend of birds and beasts, and, in herself, incarnates all that the poet holds within the scope of imagination.

Having abandoned the idea of finding gold, that too easily assumed symbol of integration, the hero of the story is unexpectedly transported into a world of wonder by the luxuriance of tropical nature, its green clouds and illusive aerial spaces. He becomes bewitched by the wilderness of the primaeval forest, as with the splendour of his inner emotions. The outer world provides living symbols: first of potential dangers of the unknown; then, as he penetrates further into the forest, strange silences, disturbed and relieved by flights of innumerable birds, many-coloured and various as emotions, and through the bird-voices a melodious human voice that calls and beckons him on. No, not quite a human voice, but of a spiritual being: Nature's own spontaneous birth; the *Kore* herself appears, an existence never to be brought to subjection; a bird-spirit, flashing into being amidst thunderstorm and lightning. At the very moment of her recognition a poisonous snake is coiled about her ankle. At the first embrace he is stricken by the touch of death.

In this story of Rima, this dweller in the Green Mansions of his soul, Hudson achieves an individual myth, telling of innermost experience. It is a long story of suffering and tragedy. Held in the grip of a peculiar fate, surrounded by the savage superstitions of native tribes, the inner drama is played, and the girl perishes by fire, her body is reduced to ashes. The earthly man survives, and at the end of the story finds a new life.

These examples of suprasensible and clairvoyant experience represent but a few of what might be chosen. By their capacity of observing and awakening senses, the authors are able to relate the phenomenal with the noumenal as true naturalists should do. This chapter is offered as a corollary to those that have gone before and come after.

CHAPTER SIX

SOME ASPECTS OF CLAIRVOYANT PERCEPTION

How do you know but that every bird that cuts its airy way
Is an immense world of delight, closed by your senses five?

BLAKE

The existence of Clairvoyant Perception has only comparatively recently been considered seriously by scientific investigation. The number of those who recognise its importance is rapidly growing. Varying kinds of extra-sensible perception have been distinguished that differentiate degrees of clairvoyance, exemplified in the following experiments.

On one side of an opaque cube is marked a figure. The observer, to whom the figure is previously unknown, is on the other side of the marked cube.

(*a*) In this case a clairvoyant observer looks at the cube from a point on the far side and opposite to that on which the figure is marked; he sees the figure on the far side of the cube in the *reverse* position, as it would be seen if the cube were transparent.

(b) The clairvoyant observer in this case would see the figure not reversed, but as though he was on the opposite side of the cube from that on which he really is.

(*c*) In this case the observer sees all sides, front and back, top and bottom of the cube simultaneously. He is able to take up several points of view. The terms back, front and sides lose significance. The consciousness of the observer in this case seems to be no longer contained within the body or brain, but as it were peripherally situated. The observer is no longer limited within his sense-perceptions. Indeed he has left his sense-organs in his stationary and physical body, and partakes of some kind of universality that is outside the stationary and physical.

That such a state of consciousness can exist among men,

although of rare occurrence, is not unrelated to the mystery of physical life. Case (*c*) carries our speculations into the purely metaphysical, and is not my immediate concern, but I shall consider what M. M. Moncrieff, in his book on *The Theory of Clairvoyant Perception,* has called "Common Perceptual Consciousness", which is dependent on the stimulation of the retina by the incident of electro-magnetic radiations, namely the radiations of light. Perceptual consciousness is subject to the limitations of the structures in front of the retina, the crystalline lens and the cornea. Moncrieff's contention is that ordinary sense-directed vision is a special and limited type of a larger clairvoyant vision. That sight, as we ordinarily understand the word, is brought about by an *inhibition.* It is a faculty that inhibits a more universal vision in order that attention may be less generally distributed, and consequently centred on particular objects, and he argues that psychic phenomena, which appear to the larger clairvoyant vision, have been repressed and discouraged in every possible way by Mediaeval Christianity. He writes: "The Church with increasing severity has tried, on the excuse of orthodoxy, to stamp out all psychic phenomena that in any way undermined the authority of the ecclesiastical hierarchy . . . Not only were many thousands of innocent people tortured and burnt at the stake by the inquisition, but many thousands were burnt in Catholic and Protestant countries up to comparatively recent times on the pretence that they were possessed of the Devil . . . As a result of these abominations in the name of religion, a very large number of individuals possessing psychic powers were exterminated, and those that survived were compelled to suppress or hide the fact that they possessed these powers." He goes on to point out that people living in Eastern countries were never subjected to anything like the same extent, to these forms of persecution in the supposed cause of religion, and that in consequence we find a larger proportion of people in these countries that possess faculties of extra-sensory perception.

The growth of the scientific outlook also accounts for the suppression of the larger clairvoyant vision. The scientific method is one of selection and measurement. It concentrates on those memories that are of immediate use, and keeps the other wide, more diffused recollections and surmises, below the threshold of consciousness. In the service of science, perception itself is the servant of immediate need, and isolates what is present-interest and use, deliberately cutting out anything that is vague and undefined. In these two ways, through the repressive action of what has passed for religion, and the selective method of modern science, the universal all-pervasive consciousness has been suppressed out of the range of our normal awareness. This suppression has become a true repression, and the energy which under less restricted conditions, has in past times and amongst Eastern races a natural outlet, has in the West produced much, if not all, of the tension and distress evident in modern society. The rising incidence of insanity in highly mechanised countries makes clear the fact that when sense-conscious, outer life is exaggerated at the expense of the less exactly defined inner activities, then the emphasis which has gone too far in one direction, compensates by swinging too far to the other.

The examples of instinctive life that have been instanced in the earlier chapters of this book give reason for believing that wholly instinctive creatures possess, in a large measure, extra-sensory perceptions, and it is probable that all living things do so. It is not necessary to multiply instances, for any reader who is familiar with animals and plants will remember the migratory urges, the strange facts of ecology, and of symbiosis, also of the movements of animals that are governed by a collective psyche. These patterns of behaviour clearly suggest perceptions that cannot be traced to the activity of physical sense-organs alone.

The note that sounds new, and perhaps startling, in Captain Moncrieff's book is that he regards the sense perceptions as we know them, seeing, touching, hearing, tasting, smelling, as limited and restricted forms of the universal clairvoyance, which he presumes to be in all living things.

For many years as a field naturalist I have surmised something of the kind. I have reached after it in a half-perceiving way, but only in the last ten years have the many and sundry patterns of animal, bird and plant behaviour with which I was familiar, become in part illuminated. They are by no means completely illuminated, and certainly I would not expect them to be, but a light has begun to shine in a region that was dim and obscure.

Two ideas stand out. (1) That there is a universal consciousness pervading all things. (2) That the sense-organs are so contrived as to limit and direct within small compass this larger consciousness. A comparison can be made with the receiving set of a radio. There is a certain relative position of parts of the mechanism which is sensitive to a small band of wave-lengths, leaving innumerable other wave-lengths unrecorded. The arrangements of the parts of the mechanism which concentrates on limited bands of wave-lengths is comparable to the activity of sense-organs.

The greater part of Moncrieff's book is concerned with the sense of sight. He is in agreement with the naive perceptual-theory as against the projective-theories and the non-spatial, visual-sensation theories; and he contends that all sight is clairvoyant, and in the first place undifferentiated, and that by our present-time human method of particularising our vision we *do* see the things we think we see. Our eyes, acting as the organs of an ego-consciousness, enable us to cut out much that would embarrass and bewilder. If we are able to accept this in relation to our organ of sight, it is not difficult to make the next step, and to think of all our organs, not only eyes and ears, as having been adapted in the process of our development to a purposeful limiting action. Our development in this particular form of human consciousness may be thought of as having passed through various stages which we may find represented not only in the lives of existing genera of animal and plant life, but also in the processes of embryological development.

If we watch carefully, as many field naturalists have done, the growth and behaviour of animals, and think of them as representing other forms, and more diffuse forms of consciousness than that of human beings, we enter into a region of vast and exciting speculation, and not only of speculation, for, as understanding grows, as the result of an active participation in the lives of the creatures, there comes a knowledge, as yet but rudimentary, of the awareness that animals have of their environment. E. S. Russell's *Behaviour of Animals* gives a most valuable selection of cases of animal activity that illustrate instinctive and automatic reactions, maintenance activities, and insight learning. In these we can trace development; consciousness in the lower animals being outside anything that to a human mind might be considered knowable, but which we must think of as a diffuse and general perception, comparable to primitive clairvoyant vision, undifferentiated by a centralising ego-personality. To make clear my meaning with an example, let us look, with what insight we can muster, at such a creature as a newly-emerged mason-bee. When its wings are dried and hardened, and it has stayed sufficiently long in the nest to feel the assurance necessary to take its first flight, it launches itself into an unknown universe. Soon it alights and rests on some chance-object – in this case the cuff of my coat. From its bright, undulled colours, I can see it is a young bee. The garden, the sky, the earth, the flowers, all that surrounds it is unexplored. I ask it: "What do you know, young bee, of the world and the universe?" It answers: "I am the universe." All that it needs is with itself. Its inner sensibilities embrace all the complicated patterns that it must, and does, naturally adopt in the world in which it is destined to function. Its consciousness partakes of some kind of universality, that links and equates its inner urges with the outer environment.

Various theories have been propounded to account for the development of living things. The mechanistic theory considers growth as the summation of particular and discreet occurrences proceeding along separate paths, independent, yet harmonious with one another. Weismann's machine-theory, various vitalistic theories have been put forward. These agree with the mechanistic theories in so far as they can consider the separate processes, but they postulate that these are coordinated by an immaterial, transcendent *entelechy*. The organismus theory is now accepted by most biologists as being more in accord with the observed facts of embryological development. The supporters of this theory seek for a governing principle within the organism, and for essences (whatever they are) within the separate organs or parts which themselves find harmonious coordination within the living system. The organism is itself a self-contained system rather than an aggregate of separate developments. It is crucial to such investigations to look to the origins, and the spot-light of research is directed on a-cellular or uni-cellular organisms, and particularly on the germ-cells. These are considered as polyphastic unitary systems; that is to say, unitary systems harmonious and coordinated in their processes.

The practice of many orthodox scientists is to look for a substance or substances which, by their presence, govern the processes in the various stages of their development. What I am suggesting is that all organs, considered as integral systems, are devised for the withholding and limitation of the diffused and universal consciousness. These are, in the same way, though in multifarious degrees, directed by forces of restricition and inhibition working within the system. They constitute the normal sense-functions with which we are familiar.

Even separate cells are such polyphastic systems, and account in their totality for the phenomenalisation of the creature. Each member-system of any individual creature can be thought of as exercising a specialising focus for the Creative

Thought. The individual creature is in this way linked with a supersensible consciousness, and through its organs perceive the world. As the organs grow more complicated in structure and function, so does the sensibility become more exact and limited within the wholeness of the individual system. The individual system grows by means of its limitations and inhibitions, and is thus able to establish a place in the world in which it functions.

There is little doubt that some animals live and function in different worlds of sense-perception from other animals. For example, the world in which a slug lives is probably two-dimensional, a duck is not always able to differentiate between parts of its own body and its environment, whereas a cat is conscious of its own bodily existence in a three-dimensional world. In a comparable way, though in varying degrees, some men live and function in other worlds of perception from that of others.

The method of biological science, which consists in the measurement of physical objects, is concerned for the most part with creatures that have reached, so far as physical and chemical orientations are concerned, an already advanced and complicated state of development. In the study of embryology, however, the biologist is forced to enter a region of indeterminacy and vagueness, with which the physicist and chemist are already familiar.

When the scientific method seeks to take hold of the sources of creation or evolution it becomes uncertain both of measurement and timing. An example of such a state of dubiety is the "Heisenberg-relation", which states that the place and velocity of an electron cannot be exactly determined simultaneously, for in order to determine the place of the electron it must be illuminated; this means that a light quantum hits it, and its momentum is altered by the impact of the light. The more accurately is the position determined, the less accurately can its velocity be measured. Such an inherent uncertainty must affect the causal law, for unless we know the present exactly, how can we calculate the future? We cannot in principle know the present in all levels of determinativeness. Such considerations in themselves define a limitation to the scientific method.

In the study of embryological development, where exact observation and analysis takes us as far as our sense-perceptions allow, it is impossible to determine an individual biological process completely without knowing the processes in all the other parts. To know these is impossible, for each processs affects every other. It therefore seems likely that there is a biological realm of indeterminacy similar to that of the Heisenberg principle in the realm of intra-atomic physics. Indeed, the situation within the living creature is even more ambiguous, since within the organism a state of complication and individuality is reached which can no longer be dealt with under physical law. A higher law must be introduced, a statistic of a higher order. Biologists are well aware of the possibility, even the probability, of such a statistic, the presence of which places the problems of biology (at any rate some of them) outside the methods of measurement and timing of physical events. The scientific method has indeed led its advocates into a region of uncertainty. By the precision of its method, the method proves inadequate to solve the problem of life. As Bergson has put it, "Intellect is not a fit instrument to deal with the processes of life and creation. Intellect deals with the known, the static, cause and effect, the old which is repeated. Each instant is a fresh endowment, the new is ever upspringing, the form just come into existence could never have been foreseen, because the causes here (in the new) are unique of their kind, are part of the effect – have come into existence with it, and are determined by it – all this we feel within ourselves, but we cannot *think* it, in the strict sense of the word, nor express it in terms of pure understanding. No wonder at that; we must remember what intellect is meant for.

The intellect lets the essential aspect of life escape, as if it were not intended to think such an object."

The method of science has, in the past, been well justified in defining its method and limitation, but, in the light of an always advancing consciousness, is it not questionable how long this method and limitation can endure? In physics and chemistry, and now in biology, science is knocking at the door of metaphysics. Bertalanffy in *Modern Theories of Development* has posed the dilemma of the modern biologist as follows:

> Thus the investigator works on the one hand with concepts which are foreign to the physical sciences, and at the same time insists that in the vital processes only physio-chemical laws are allowed. The fact that concepts creep in which give a special place to organisms, which they cannot have foretold according to its own principles, constitutes a striking refutation of mechanism in its traditional form.

The necessity of a metaphysical interpretation makes itself increasingly evident, and although some biologists still repudiate imaginative or intuitive interpretations of the mystery of life, and take their stand on the position that the life-mystery is beyond explaining, and that the logic of biology and the theory of life should be regarded as totally unrelated; yet intuitive interpretations are inevitable, as being themselves a part of the increasing human consciousness *which is both the instrument and the field of our discovery*. Man is man, and cannot escape from this human capacity for growth in consciousness. The arches of his inner life under-prop the outer arches of the surrounding universe which human sense-perceptions discover; his very thought is a part of the universal and creative thought.

The oneness of human individual consciousness with a collective or a divine and creative consciousness is an assumption that springs spontaneously, though in different guises, in all such human activities as psychology, philosophy and religion, and though the gulf between religion and science may at the present time appear to many men as unbridgeable, there are signs in such borderland regions as psychology and aesthetics that the gulf yawns not so wide as it did fifty years ago.

With such thoughts in mind it will be well to review some of the recent biological research into the processes of life; and in particular into the processes of growth as manifest in embryology and other forms of active metamorphosis. These may cast some light – or some shadows – on the theme of instinct and the linking of instinct with physiological processes, and on the aspect in which these may reveal themselves in the light of clairvoyant, super-sensible perception.

CHAPTER SEVEN

SELF-EXPANDING SYSTEMS

Some of us should venture to embark on a synthesis of facts and theories, albeit with the second-hand and incomplete knowledge of some of them – and at the risk of making fools of ourselves.

E. SCHRODINGER

What a man desires to know is that. *(the external world) But his means of knowing is* this. *(himself) How can he know* that? *Only by* this.

THE SCHOOL OF CH'I

The growth of any organism is always a metamorphosis; in some cases the changes that take place are so gradual that one phase follows in simple-seeming sequence on another, but in other cases the changes are surprising, radical and complete. The study of embryology comprises the sequence of structural and functional changes that arise from the fertilisation of the ovum until the end-structure is reached. Within this process of growth, organs develop in relation to each other. From the beginning the formative movements of development are essentially movements of a self-expanding system. Even single cells are self-expanding systems, and the secondary system of organs within the main organism passively and obediently follow the motions of the larger system. Yet it has been demonstrated that there would seem to be hiatuses or breaks separating one stage or growth from another. The cell divisions or cleavages would seem in some cases to be irrelevant to the organ-regions that follow in later stages of development. Experimental embryology seeks to find out how much or how little, stages in one phase of development are dependent on processes at a previous stage.

In the great majority of cases of embryological development

fertilisation is necessary. The male and female gametes, or germ cells, meet and fuse, and from the resulting zygote the embryo develops. The meeting of the gametes, when both ova and sperm are cast at hazard into the sea, would seem to be a matter of chance, yet these cells, these half-organisms, seem unable, as a rule, to develop without meeting with the other. They are already endowed with methods of behaviour which, in some cases, seem highly specialised to their conditions. So remarkable is this behaviour, and so impossible is it to think of these single cells as endowed with intelligence, as that word is usually understood, that if we are to account for their behaviour at all, we must assume their activities are altogether due to automatic, self-directed mechanisms – or that they have some kind of clairvoyant way of recognising their condition and reacting to it. To give an illustration of such behaviour, the egg and sperm of certain star-fish may be cited. The unfertilised yet mature egg of the star-fish is, when it is cast into the sea, surrounded by a thin layer of jelly, which presumably might offer some small protection to an otherwise naked egg. The sperm are attracted to the egg, and swarm round the jelly-covering. By their own efforts they are unable to penetrate it, and so are not able to reach the egg, which is the *raison d'être* of their existence. The egg, when surrounded by the sperm, which are unable to reach it, would seem to become *aware* of their presence. It is able to shoot out a very fine protoplasmic filament towards one of the sperm that is in contact with the outside of the jelly zone.* This filament catches the sperm at its anterior end, in much the same way as a fish that is caught on a line, so the sperm struggles to free itself. Sometimes it does free itself, but usually it is drawn through the

* It can be argued that the balance of Hyaluronidise and Hyaluronic acid alone condition the impregnation of the ovum. No doubt such factors are present; chemical determinants are part of the mechanism of life; but can it be imagined that they can account for the flinging out of the fishing-line filament, and the capturing of the sperm? The postulation of a primitive clairvoyance will to many men be a more satisfactory explanation.

jelly to the periphery of the egg, where the fine membranes of the egg rise to meet and engulf it.

In the presence of this mysterious happening, the observer, if he is looking for a materialistic explanation, and is anxious to explain life in terms of chemistry and physics, presumes a *substance* diffused from the sperm through the jelly, that stimulates the out-throwing of the filament.

At this early stage in reproduction the sperm is a part of the environment of the ovum. I would suggest that they are united in a larger unit of activity than they themselves, considered separately, comprise. This activity does not lend itself to explanation in terms of chemical and physical reactions any more easily than does the fig-wasp explain the formation of the gall-flowers in the fig, for the latter are formed before the wasp which is to lay its eggs in the gall makes its arrival within the synconium. It may, however, be cogently argued that the life in the wasp is intimately associated, and even integrated, with the life of the fig tree. In both cases, that of fig and wasp and of the echinoderm egg and the echinoderm sperm, we are witnessing activities which may be considered as partial expressions of a total situation, of which only the physical manifestation has been partially apprehended; the total noumenon of the situation transcends the physical and phenomenal expression. Such a statement may seem an easy way of avoiding the *causal* aspects of a situation. It may be, however, that a-causal happenings are here more in evidence than causal ones, for an enormous number of facts suggest unified and governing activities amongst organisms, as, for example, those that relate gall-flies with their host plants, and with the equilines that associate with the gall-fly larvae within the galls. We find indeed staggering complexities of inter-relationships of organisms of different kinds.

If we look for *substances* which may be the organisers of such relationships, and there is considerable evidence that such substances have been defined and isolated, then we must ask from whence do such substances arise? The defining of a substance only throws the question back; from whence? It is known that the balance of Hyaluronidise and Hyaluronic acid conditions the impregnation of an ovum. Yes, but what is the valency of these chemical substances within the noumenal reality of the *inception of life?*

Are we to suppose that the physio-chemical substances contain the whole of the life-impulse, or do they merely constitute the material manifestation? Many questions present themselves: how are such critical cytoplasmic substances as Hyaluronidise and Hyaluronic acid to be differentiated from the less active substances of the organism? Of what nature are hormones and enzymes?

The same method of thought that has produced Marxian and Darwinian theory dominates the greater part of modern physio-chemical research, and seems determined to demonstrate the processes of life as purely mechanistic. Substances, so it is believed, will be able to account for all processes of growth.

Considerable advances have been made along analytical lines, and the question, "What are enzymes?" has been in part answered. The chromosomes which carry out what has been termed the stuff of heredity contain a special substance, deoxyribonucleic acid, which, for short, is indicated by the letters DNA. This DNA of the nucleus of a cell contains, in coded form, a kind of blue-print of all the information, so it is assumed, needed to assemble in a reproduced cell all that is contained in the original cell before division, and from subsequent individual cells all the cells that go to make the entire mature organism.

That the structure of DNA has great significance there can be no doubt, for its characteristic as bearer of information accords well with a mechanistic interpretation of life. It carries messages as to how a cell is to develop and proliferate. It can produce exact copies of itself and it appears that of all the substances of an organism, only this substance has the power of replication. Cells of course contain much more than their nuclei, cytoplasm, chloroplasts, etc., and far smaller units, too small for the ordinary microscope; the most important of these minute particles are the enzymes and the microsomes which are genetically controlled. The microsomes follow the DNA construction, with the addition of ribonucleic acid, termed RNA. It has been shown that RNA can manufacture enzymes, while DNA cannot. These discoveries go towards demonstrating the mechanism of growth; but it has not yet been shown how DNA can make the microsomal RNA. In all this elaborate and exacting research there is manifest a desire, an urge, one might call it, to reduce life to material physico-chemical actions and reactions. If this could be done then men might produce life itself. Goethe anticipated the idea of the homunculus being manufactured in a glass retort; but poetic understanding prompted that, with the true coming into existence of this little monster, he and his retort should be swept away in the ocean waves of unconsciousness under the prow of Galatea's boat.

What is it that makes it so difficult for the modern biologist to admit the reality of a spiritual counterpart to this world that is perceived by the senses? It is surely most admirable that the physical objects be examined with scrupulous care; but the particular slant that Marx and Darwin have given to the direction of much modern thought may very well not be the way to the right understanding of life. As Dr Jung has put it: "When any natural human function gets lost, i.e. is denied conscious intentional expression, a general disturbance results. Hence it is quite natural that with the triumph of the Goddess of Reason a general neuroticising of modern man should set in, a dissociation of personality analogous to the splitting of the world to-day by the iron curtain. This boundary line bristling with barbed wire *runs through the psyche of modern* *man, no matter on which side he lives."** Modern biology, despite its meticulous examination of physical development, in so far as it is atheistic, and so denies the natural functions of feeling and intuition, is self-contained, restricted and barren. It leads to the devaluation of the human psyche, and consequently to the sterilisation of consciousness itself. Only with the aid of Mephistopheles was the pedantic Wagner able to produce the glass-bottle homunculus, destined for self-destruction, and even longing for destruction.

Coincident with the work of the chemists, large numbers of experiments have been made by embryologists which by isolating individual organisms, or portions of organisms, seek to discover the principles of growth. For example, what substance can be found to produce parthenogenetic development, or what portion of the fertilised or unfertilised egg can develop if portions of the egg are removed. These experiments, interesting and valuable as the results may be, do not by the nature of their method, consider the whole creature within its environment; they study but portions of creatures, or portions of living organs, treated within the restricted circumstances of the experiment. Within this method, factors of development have been most carefully studied.

The characteristics that are transmitted from the parents to the developing egg are called internal factors that, in the course of development, enter into relation with the external influences of the environment. Such a statement is over simple, in that it assumes that the internal factors are *all* present in the fertilised egg, making of the egg a container of a self-unfolding blue-print. It would seem that they were *not* all present as a comparatively simple experiment shows. If at the two-cell stage of a developing frog's egg one blastomere, as the cells of the early cleavages are called, is killed and left attached, the other living blastomere will develop into a half embryo. If, however the dead blastomere is removed, the remaining one

* *The Undiscovered Self.*

regulates itself, and develops into a whole embryo. This would suggest that one of the blastomeres, in the presence of a dead blastomere, will produce half an embryo if the dead blastomere is still attached. Now the presence of this dead blastomere is not a factor which existed as such in the egg. It may be considered as part of the developing environment, whose presence inhibits normal growth.

A deduction is that the living blastomere is able to *perceive* the environment, and that its behaviour is determined by the presence or absence of the dead blastomere. This speck of living material is able to develop, is indeed forced to develop, into either a complete or half embryo, according as it is attached or not attached to the dead blastomere.

The problem remains: are material substances responsible, or are we here witnessing a clairvoyant perception, playing within the living blastomere from out a universal consciousness, a light shining in the particular darkness of a humanly conducted laboratory experiment?

No very large jump of the imagination is needed for comparison with the case of nematocysts of the coelenterates and the ingesting organs of the sea-slug. In some cases the nematocyst explodes; in other conditions, namely with the bodies of other specially organised sea-slugs, the minute though highly organised stinging-cell perceives, within this specialised environment, a governing activity, reciprocal to both coelenterate and mollusc. Its behaviour is determined in accordance with ideas, to use Professor Whitehead's phrase, proper to the organism in question, proper to the activity of organism and the environment, namely, of the ingested nematocyst and the enveloping body of the mollusc.

After an egg has been fertilised and the nucleus of the spermatozoon has fused with the nucleus of the ovum, cleavage takes place and the egg is split up into a number of blastomeres, and these in the process of development give rise to the development of different and differentiating regions of the embryo. It has been proved that the blastomeres during cleavage are effectively identical, and that the cause of subsequent differentiation is not to be found in the division of the original nucleus. Now it has been found in primitive creatures such as echinoderms that if blastomeres are artificially separated off, they have the same potency to develop as the original ovum, provided the separation has been made before or at the sixteenth blastomere stage. The size of the embryo in the cases of such separation is of course smaller than the normal through insufficiency of material; but the material within the developing embryo, even though small, appears to be toti-potent. It is also noted that the proportions of the developing parts in the small embryo are normal, and so we may regard the embryos, however small, as being equipotent systems, in which the destiny of any developing blastomere is independent of the position it occupied in the original embryo. Its destiny is determined by the *position* it actually does occupy in the developing embryo. It would seem that there was a kind of awareness of one blastomere with another within the totality of the developing embryo, a totality of feeling, or clairvoyant perception, activating the creature that is growing towards the totality of an inherent idea.

Those workers who are looking for a mechanistic interpretation postulate the existence of some directing *substance* within the cell, the DNA already mentioned. The hypothesis of some kind of clairvoyant perception among the cells of any organism is put forward as an alternative to the *substance* idea, and postulates a noumenal *gestaltung* principle as being more in accordance with facts than the hypothesis of merely physico-chemical reactions. These latter are however demonstrably present, and should be accepted as the physical mechanism through which the totality of the situation is manifested.

Holding the above hypothesis in mind it may be

instructive to regard the development of certain parasitic worms.

In some Ascidians there is evidence that the raw material of the protoplasm is qualitatively sorted out in different blastomeres; in other groups of ascidians the blastomeres have equivalent cytoplasm. Those in which all the blastomeres are equivalent are called regulation-eggs, namely, eggs from which a whole embryo will develop; the others, which are qualitatively different, are called mosaic-eggs, for their development is as though from a mosaic, where different portions of the growing larva develop from different blastomeres. From these observations we may deduce that in some groups the separated blastomeres contain the whole potential, and in other groups that the formative principle has already become localised.

What mysterious potential is at work? Bergson's question addressed to instinct is apposite to the happening within the developing embryo: "If we could ask it, and it could reply, it would render up to us the most intimate secrets of the universe." In the same way as the instinctive animal is closely bound in its behaviour to its environment, so we may see the developing blastomeres related one with another, clairvoyantly perceptive to the potentials of their environment, namely, the other blastomeres.

In some species of the creatures in question, the Ascidians, the protoplasm of the separate blastomeres contains the whole potential of development; in others it is partially divided. Here we might seem to be near that critical phase of division where the mosaic forms of development separate from the toti-potent, and our imaginations, pausing to gaze in deep wonder, are near to the untrodden ground indicated by Mephistopheles to Faust, when he seeks the very foundations of existence in the regions of the mysterious Mothers.

Untrodden ground,
Where none may tread, a way that must be found
Beyond all finding, prayed for past all prayer,
Thither if you are ready, and can dare.

Into this region Faust descends to seek what may be sought by the poet within the influence of "The Eternal Mind's eternal recreation."

In contrast to such dramatic and imaginative speculations, we may consider de Beer's strictly scientific statement: "The cytoplasmic raw material mosaic-eggs are organ-forming substances. Sometimes they are visible, as in the case of the Ascidian styele where a yellow substance is necessary for the formation of muscle-fibres. Others are invisible. On the other hand, eggs are not wanting in which certain visible substances are present, and in which development is always distributed to certain cells. Yet when these eggs are centrifuged and the visible substance in question is completely disarranged, normal larvae are nevertheless produced. The experiment of centrifuging shows that these substances are not localised organ-forming materials. On the other hand, in the case of Styele, centrifuging upsets the development."

To turn again from the scientist to the philosopher-poet:

Down to the depths then! or perhaps the heights!
It's all the same! Far from the actual,
Into the world of freedom and of form.

The problem lies in both cases in the relation between the external and internal forces. The scientist must be concerned with what can be measured, or rather what can be approached with the idea of measurement. The poet, looking within himself, finds his problem interiorised. Both agree that the internal factors of development, or perception, can only exert their influence in association with external factors. These latter are the more easily perceived, and offer the first point of vantage in any investigation. Yet even in the acts of perception there are hidden difficulties, for when we look closely at seemingly external factors, their properties are seen in an uncertain light. Gravity, which is regarded by de Beer as an external quality, as it must be so regarded by any biologist, is to the physicist a force acting *within* the material. Eddington has written: "We need not regard matter as a foreign entity causing disturbance in the gravitational field: the disturbance *is* matter. In the same way we do not regard light as an intruder in the electromagnetic field, causing the electromagnetic force to oscillate; the oscillation constitutes the light. Nor is heat a fluid causing agitation of the molecules of a body; the agitation is heat." To the same intent, Meister Eckhardt, a thirteenth century mystic whose philosophical writings were concerned with the relation between God and human thought, has written: "It is all inside, not outside, for everything is inside."

The gravitational field contains the world, and the egg, that we are observing. They are related; yet it has been shown that gravity does not determine the axis of certain eggs, since the axis has been established while yet in the ovary. Once determined, however, the yolk, which is heavier than the rest of the contents of the egg, sinks, and in this way gravity ensures the vertical position; and the first cleavage always passes through the vertical axis. In this way the gravitational relation, within the environment, influences the first cleavage, and consequently subsequent cleavages.

Temperature has an important influence on the development of eggs. Low temperature can inhibit any development, and temperature lower than normal in the incubation of birds' eggs can produce growth without the normal differentiation. Temperatures that are markedly above the normal also produce abnormalities. Different temperatures applied to different parts of the growing embryo, produce abnormal developments. The environmental influence impinges on the internal factors, changing or promoting, or inhibiting their development. The facts of relatedness of external and internal factors should, I suggest, be regarded not merely as chemical and physical reactions but as an *actual, perceptual reciprocity within the universe of ideas, a reciprocity between the mystery of life and an emergent consciousness, activated not only from the centre of growth within the organism, but also under the inevitable peripheral, cosmic influence.* It is impossible to contemplate, in any philosophic or imaginative sense, a centre, without contemplating, in the same thought, a circumference. All too readily have investigators supposed that a growing point is in itself self-sufficient, as do many bio-chemists who claim that DNA contains a packaged blueprint of future development.

In the normal development of an egg, the first segmentations form a solid ball of cells, called morula. (This can be much modified where yolk is present.) At a later stage it becomes a hollow ball called a blastula, and an opening pore of this ball is called a blastopore. In the course of development the blastopore changes its position, and it has been found that the dorsal lip of the blastopore is a very critical area, in that this dorsal lip determines the position of the axial structures that are to develop; and it does more than that, for if the dorsal lip of the blastopore of one embryo be grafted on to the flank of another, it will induce the formation there of axial organs, which would otherwise never have arisen.

In the experiment of grafting the lip of the blastopore of one embryo on to another, two growing points are put in juxtaposition, and the peripheral influences are altered; or, to put the statement of this happening in more orthodox terms, there are two "organisers" in close relation within the growing organism. Remarkable is the fact that organisers from different embryos of different species can, by artificial grafting, be made to grow within one organism, the lip of the blastopore exerting an extraordinary influence on the neighbouring tissues.

More extraordinary still, and, I think, partially enlightening, is the fact that it is not the *substance* of the tissue composing the dorsal lip of the blastopore which acts as the organiser, but the tissue which is grafted into it that acts as organiser. This would suggest the influence of supra-polar forces acting from supra-polar regions. De Beer comes near to this thought (though he might well repudiate it) when he writes: "The determination of the organiser therefore suggests the effect of *gradients* established with regard to the form of the whole organism, i.e. the relation of the whole egg, the egg-axis, and the point of entrance of the sperm, and regardless of the actual *substance* at any place." (Italics are mine.) This picture drawn by de Beer assumes an only slightly different significance when the organism is regarded as a being open to peripheral and cosmic influences.

This may seem, and is, vague enough; but we needs must be vague when we are studying the emergent mystery of life itself, and here it may be well to remember Bergson's saying: "Intellect lets the essential aspect of life escape, as if it were not intended to think such an object." If this is so, then there must be some other function capable of apprehension and I would suggest *feeling* and *intuition* must come to our aid. The biologist must *feel* himself into the material of his study, and this many biologists have done. Lawrence Henderson has written: "In some obscure manner cosmic and biological evolution are one. In short, we are led to the assumption that the generic or evolutionary processes, both cosmic and biological, when considered in certain aspects, constitute a single orderly development that yields results not merely contingent, but resembling those which in human action we regard as purposeful. For undeniably, two things which are related together in a complex manner by a reciprocal fitness make, in a very real sense, a unit – something quite different from the two alone, or the sum or the two, or the relationship between the two. In human affairs such a unit arises only from the effective operation of purpose." Professor Wood Jones, commenting on this passage, writes: "We have now arrived at the stage of thought from which all dictates of scientific prudence should prompt us to withdraw. Nevertheless, the development of this line of thought has seemed to be so natural, and to be so inevitably forced on us by the evidence of facts that it is difficult to turn back." And again: "The biologist must try to see, not only the whole organism, but must regard this organism in its whole natural setting. Might the human philosopher aspire to see the universe as a whole? . . . . What has become known as the Gestalt Theory is the great intellectual quest of mankind."

To return to the problem of the organiser and the areas of its influence. Organisation can spring from one centre, as it usually does, or from two, as in the case of ingrafting, where they show an independent differentiation with regard to the axial structures. The growing organism is also, of course, related to the external factors, though sometimes in a perplexing way. For example; the eye-cup of certain amphibia can develop, if transplanted to inappropriate portions of the developing embryo.

The situation within the growing creature is complicated and bafflingly mysterious. Students of embryology are at the beginning of discoveries, and workers in this field, those inclining towards a physio-chemical interpretation, and those who regard life as an interplay between the centre of apparent growth and the cosmic periphery, should be unwilling, out of hand, to reject each other's methods. The goal of their search may well prove to be one, even though it ever recedes beyond the world of sense-perception into the world of ideas.

Both facts and inferences contained in the preceding chapter will be seen by any reader as largely contradictory. This does not mean that any of the workers in these fields are in error as regards their facts. The facts demonstrate, however, that the mystery of physical life is deep and evasive, and that the intellectual approach is met, again and again, with contradiction. Miguel de Unamuno is reported to have said: "If a man never contradicts himself, the reason must be that he virtually never says anything at all," and Cardinal Nicholas of Cusa, speaking of God or of Life, he hardly distinguishes between them, declares as a personal experience: "And I have found that the place wherein Thou art found unveiled is girt round with the coincidence of contradictories." Such sayings do not lead to silence or to acquiescence. Men will ever seek for the source of the Sacred Fount. When they find themselves girt round with the contradictories, they know that they may be on the path, and as their steps proceed, they gather confidence.

CHAPTER EIGHT

THE ENIGMA OF PHYSICAL DEATH

The creative act, alike in its power and importance, is eschatological.

N. BERDYAEV

Biology finds in living things processes of change. The protoplasm in the cells, in the act of living, gives off waste products; the cells divide, and new cells come from the divisions of the old. Within the limitations of their formal patterns, all creatures live, digest, excrete, store and expend energy. These processes happen for a time, then cease in death. The study of life is bounded, as far as the investigations of science are concerned, with that which happens between birth and death.

The void beyond, toward which all life tends, is the greatest of all human enigmas, one on which much thought and fancy has been expended. Science, so far as science has yet advanced, can find nothing to record in the dead body but decomposition. Yet by the study of the living body much can be learnt about physical death. One of its most striking conclusions is that within the tissues of the physical body there lurks a potential of deathlessness. In each individual cell, there is a spark of immortality.

The non-cellular and uni-cellular animals and plants portray this potential immortality in its most obvious forms. Many of these creatures reproduce by a process of division. They divide into two parts, each part taking a portion of the original substance to make two, new, smaller individuals. These in turn grow larger, and again divide; in this way, what was at first one, becomes many; the original substance spreads itself out, and does not perish, except through accidental causes such as unpropitious changes in its environment, or predatory foes.

There is no natural, unaccidental death for these primitive forms of life.

Paramecium, a ciliated infusorian, a unicellular animal of comparatively simple structure, having a cell-wall, with fine hair-like processes called cilia, has been kept under observation for many generations. L. L. Woodruff has demonstrated that this little animal is able to reproduce itself without experiencing conjugation, and is potentially immortal. He has shown that the original substance of an individual, though it divides again and again, does not necessarily perish, but continues to live. Death, though it may be accidental, is not an inevitable part of its fate. Woodruff observed *Paramecium* for more than eight thousand, five hundred generations, during which time (thirteen and a half years), there was no conjugation, which means that the original substance was in no way added to by another individual of the same species. During this time the individuals that resulted from the repeated divisions remained healthy. Such a series of generation, if translated into human terms, would represent some millions of years. During this time there was no natural death. Each individual, as it became mature, divided into two that again divided. In the course of such an experiment vast numbers were disposed of, and Woodruff calculated that if he had been able to keep them all alive, and all their potential descendants, they would have produced a volume of matter equal to ten thousand times the volume of the earth, and that the rate of growth at the end of fifteen years would be extending its circumference into space with the velocity of light. From this we clearly see how life and death balance to make existence possible on earth. The many die by accident, but the potential of life appears immortal. And, of course not only with *Paramecium* but also with other species similar results have been obtained. For unicellular organisms there is no natural death, except in one or two unusual cases, as for example, the lactic-acid bacteria, which, as the result of its metabolism, produces an acid which, when it reaches a certain percentage in the milk in which the bacteria live, will kill the bacteria which produced the excretion. In this case death may be said to be natural and inevitable.

Reproduction by simple division is not confined to simple unicellular organisms; animals of comparatively simple structure such as planarian worms can bud off portions of themselves, and these divide into two separate creatures. The original substance is diluted with each division, but cannot be said to die. Reproduction can be in other cases without the formation of sex-cells, and though this is comparatively rare amongst higher animals, is common among plants. The apple, plum and pear trees of cultivation offer examples of agamic reproduction. The trees grow old and die, but the graft lives on in a young stock. In the same way graftings can be made from these younger plants, and they will survive after the parent-trees have died. Yet in the higher multicellular animals death appears to be the natural destiny of living things. Investigations have shown that the deaths of individuals are not caused by the constitution of their parts. All species have what would seem to be an allotted span of days, weeks or years, what might be considered their destined span, and yet when their constituent tissues are studied, there is found within them a concealed potential of immortality.

In the higher animals, the new individuals of each succeeding generation are produced by the union of ova and spermatozoa (germ-cells). At an early stage of embryological development these germ-cells remain localised and recognisable. They have a different fate from the cells that give rise to the organs of the body. These latter die at the end of the individual life, and so also do those germ-cells which happen to be contained in the body at the time. All these may be said to die by accident, as will be shown. The germ-cells which have united with other germ-cells develop into new individuals, and so carry on the potential of life from generation to generation. The discontinuity of existence, as demonstrated by the succession of generations, does not appertain to life itself, but only to the bodies of multicellular animals and plants. Life survives untouched by death, though it would seem that death claims the bodies of the higher animals as the price they pay for their specialisation of structure and function. Life has continued from the beginning until now, untouched by death.

But not only are the germ-cells found to be potentially immortal. Experiments have proved that the tissues of the bodies of higher animals are, if kept under the special conditions of laboratory experiments, also immortal; although in the natural course of events, these tissues, if left entire and functioning in the normal way, would have died. If portions of them are separated from the living bodies, and kept in appropriate conditions, they will continue living (in a restricted way) indefinitely. M. T. Burrows has succeeded in cultivating the cells of the nervous system, of the heart, and of muscle-tissues of an embryo chick, outside the body. Dr A. Carrel has shown that cells taken from most of the organs of dogs, cats, rats, guinea-pigs and man can be cultivated in suitable media outside the bodies of their original possessors. He has kept cultures of chick-embryo alive for a long period of years, far exceeding the life of a hen. These experiments hint at the probability of a potential immortality of the body cells. Within the naturally fuctioning body of the animal they die; but in artificial and appropriate conditions they survive.

What then is it that brings about death in normal conditions?

Various theories have been advanced. Weismann in 1881 suggested that death was an adaptation advantageous to the race, and had arisen, and was preserved by natural selection. At that date, the theory of natural selection was being worked pretty hard, but to-day few biologists would carry it this far. Metchinikoff maintained that death was the result of auto-intoxication resulting from the absorption of poisons from the alimentary canal. This theory no longer has the strength it once appeared to have, since rats and other creatures have been made to live completely aseptic lives, and death has still occurred at the usual time. Johannes Muller has said that death is inherent and innate, and to this statement we find a parallel in Freud's "death-instinct", of which I shall have more to say. H. M. Benedict, working on the senility of plants, has reached the same conclusion: ". . that the duration of life is directly linked with the degree of permeability in that part of the living cell which places it in contact with the universe about it, and that as life proceeds, the cell is gradually entombed by a decrease in the permeability of its protoplasm"; and he proceeds: "While decreasing permeability furnishes a possible explanation of the more obvious symptoms of senility, it cannot be the only factor of first rank. All protoplasmic functions must be involved. Underlying these primary causes of senile degeneration, there must be some general fundamental cause from which they spring. The fundamental cause may well be the colloidal nature of protoplasm."

These postulates are not at variance with the conclusions of Raymond Pearl and Leo Loeb, and carry interesting implications. Pearl sees in the *differentiation* of the organism the cause of death. Differentiation demands harmony between different parts, and should this be interrupted, one set of organs will be weakened in relation to the others, and will break down before the rest. This actually happens, and is the cause of illness and death. In close agreement, Loeb writes: "Death is not inherent in the individual cell, but is only the fate of the complicated organisms in which different types of cells or tissues are dependent on each other. It seems to happen that one or certain types of cells produce a substance or substances which gradually become harmful to a vital organ . . . or that certain tissues consume or destroy substances that are needful for the life of some or certain organs."

In reading this statement one wonders why biological science should have such assurance when postulating substances, and should be so shy of letting the imagination embrace the idea of unseen influences. Life is itself invisible, and both life and death may well be determined by invisible forces.

H. S. Jennings, an American biologist, writes on the life and death of unicellular organisms.

> As individuals the infusoria do not die save by accident. Those which we now see under our microscope have been living since the beginning of life, they come from divisions of previously existing individuals. But in just the same sense, it is true of ourselves that everyone that is alive now has been alive since the beginning of life. This truth applies at least to our bodies which are alive now; every cell of our bodies is a piece of one or more cells which existed earlier, and thus our entire body can be traced in an unbroken chain as far back into time as life goes. The difference is that in man and other higher organisms there have been left along the way great masses of cells that did not continue to live. These masses that wore out and died are what we call the bodies of the persons of earlier generations; but our own bodies are not descended by cell-division from these; they are continuations of cells that have kept on living and multiplying from the earliest times, just as have the existing infusoria.

In this manner a biologist looks at the unbroken continuity of life, and sees death as an almost accidental happening, yet as a universal happening, arising from the differentiation of the creature that has achieved specialisation. This conclusion is confirmed and elaborated by Raymond Pearl who writes: "We may fairly say, I believe, that the potential immortality of all essential cellular elements of that body has been either fully demonstrated, or else has been carried far enough to make the probability very great that properly conducted experiments would demonstrate the continuance of the life of the cells in culture to any definite extent . . . What I am leading to is the broad generalisation, perhaps not yet completely demonstrated, but with regard to Leo Loeb's work, so near it as to make little risk inhere in predicting the final outcome, *that all essential tissues of the metazoan body are potentially immortal.*" And further: "*It is the differentiation and specialisation of function of mutually dependent aggregates of cells and tissues which constitute the metazoan body which brings about death, and no inherent or inevitable mortal process in the individual cells themselves.*"

Such then is one conclusion when we consider death and immortality within the primitive substance of protoplasm. Life is seen to be continuous and unbroken from the beginning, even until now. The *forms* of life change and pass, but when these forms reach a certain standard of elaboration, they die, although the life which generated them continues.

Dr Sigmund Freud in his book *Beyond the Pleasure Principle* suggested that what he named *the death principle* was inherent and coincident with what in his earlier books he had called the pleasure-principle, and which, in these earlier works, he claimed to be the determining factor in all animal and human behaviour. Here was something, hidden yet potent in all life, even from the earliest stages, which grew, both in significance and power, and which to a large extent reversed the too-simple doctrine that sexual pleasure was the goal, either hidden or open, that ruled the destinies of men. He emphasised that in the practice of psychoanalysis he found that his patients were experiencing something passively within their souls, without exerting any influence of their own, and that they met their particular and individual fateful experience over and over again. In the light of such observations he makes the assumption that there really exists in the psychic life a repetition-compulsion, which goes beyond the pleasure-principle, and this he found to be associated with a desire for death.

When we consider these conclusions of Freud and the subsequent conclusions of other practising psychologists, and to view them in juxtaposition with the conclusions of the biologists who have been experimenting on the immortality of protoplasm, and who in the process of their research have found that when particular organs and tissues are differentiated, these organs take on, together with the elaboration of their structure, the inevitability of death; and when we seek for a harmony between these different fields of research, we are led to believe that the death-principle of Freud is the same principle that produces the differentiation of organs and tissues, and so has brought about evolution from the simple and undifferentiated to the elaboration and diversity of higher animals and plants. The creative evolutionary urge is in this way made evident in the increase of differentiation in tissues and organs. Within itself it carries, in a deeply mysterious manner, what we must think of as the death-principle; that inescapable destiny of earthly life, so far as life has developed beyond the most primitive forms.

Goethe in his botanical studies represented the growth of the plant as a rhythmical harmony of expansions and contractions; first there is upward and outward growth of stem and leaves, then the contracting into the bud, the further expansion of the flower, and the final contraction into fruit and seed.

In physical science everything is viewed as vibration or, in more general terms, as movement. All growth can be considered as *movement of exteriorisation, or movement of interiorisation*. "These forces are manifest in the life-in-death (or if one prefers, the death-in-life), flow of biological existence. Each organ in a living body would have an unlimited growth (movement of exteriorisation), were it not for the mysterious anti-bodies in the blood that destroy and, in destroying, control them. These anti-bodies, besides being always present, can arise at need, as for example in pregnancy; as soon as a female is pregnant, an anti-body to the embryo is formed (movement of interiorisation) to prevent it growing to monstrous size, and at the same time another anti-body is formed to control the growth of the placenta. The balance of healthy existence is maintained between the expanding movement of exteriorisation, and the controlling movement of interiorisation. Life and death principles are thus seen to form a balance, though one that is ever changing, within the existence of the individual.

And not only in the physical but in the life of the mind the same principle holds sway. Nietzsche, the exact thinker, the professor of Philology, in his attack on Socrates in his book *The Twilight of the Gods,* declared that thought itself, consciousness, was a form of decadence. He whose natural bent was introspection swung into the opposite and became the advocate of irreflective, spontaneous energy, thus compensating for his life as a scholar. Life, unchecked – the life of the blond beast – presented itself as the ideal. The Nazi leaders who were themselves so deeply involved in the Nihilistic Revolution seized on this part of Nietzsche's Philosophy, while ignoring much else.

The same thought, though expressed with less violence, is to be found in Shakespeare's *Hamlet,* where Hamlet is made weak and undecided by the wealth of his awareness and the richness of his thought.

> *And thus the native hue of resolution*
> *Is sicklied o'er with the pale cast of thought.*

In this way consciousness itself can be presented as a manifestation of that principle which Freud has described as that which works within us as irrespective of our conscious desires, and which he has named the death-principle, but which, paradoxically, leads us on to greater awarenese. In his estimation it is more potent in determining the fate of the individual than the pleasure-principle, which he had earlier considered as responsible for all human behaviour.

In relation to such findings as these, it is interesting to note that most of the great religions and philosophies offer a tragic interpretation of both the individual and the collective destiny. The King, or the God, must die. This idea can be traced from the primitive fertility cults, through various stages, to an ultimate crystallisation in the Christian doctrine of atonement. The wisdoms of the world unite in declaring that Man's fate is a tragic fate. Only in decadent societies, and in societies overripe for their fall, do men look for comfort to the belief that merely humanistic philosophies can bring to birth Utopias. The essential pattern is one of life-in-death or death-in-life, and the more developed the consciousness, the more obviously is the death-principle seen to be the governing and directing power.

For the believing Christian the death-principle expands into the perplexing, contradictory and half-revealed promise of the way, the truth and the life of the Christ-principle. Freud, being a materialist, saw it as a power deeply inwoven in the destinies of all men, a gift and an anguish, never quite to be apprehended, never to be stilled. The Christian is fortunate if he sees it in a slightly different way. Reading the Gospels he finds that the death-principle is here presented as the principle of love.

Christian love is the power which, through hidden and unexpected ways, determines the pattern of individual evolution. To put it another way: Love is an essential part of the pattern ordained by the urge towards greater awareness. The word love in the English language is a word used to mean diverse and sometimes contradictory states of emotion. The Greeks had two words to express what we have compacted into one: *eros*, and *agape*. Each has its meaning, yet we, using our single word, vaguely find in love a mandrake power; one root sunk deep in desire, clinging to the earth and all that the earth means for us; the other, although never separated from the original stock, penetrates dispersingly into the unknown of inner emotional experience, and finds a contradictory kind of existence in denying the simple instinctive affirmations of life. This would seem to be part of the inward directed movement. Poets have made guesses in hints and metaphors as to the nature of romantic love. Within its circle the contradictory impulses of consciousness and life meet. In this way it unites the opposites. This meeting place has been called the "Germinal Vesicle", "The Heavenly Heart", "The Terrace of Life", "The Altar on which Consciousness and Life are made" and many other names. In this region familiar landscapes fade, and the inward moving impulse pressing in towards "The Field of the Square Inch", "The Space of Former Heaven", takes on the qualities of both love and death.

This state of ecstasy John Keats has well expressed in one of his sonnets.

> *I know this being's lease*
> *My fancy to its utmost blisses spreads;*
> *Yet could I on this very midnight cease,*
> *And the world's gaudy ensign see in shreds;*
> *Verse, Fame and Beauty are intense indeed,*
> *But Death intenser–Death is Life's high meed.*

Dr Jung in his commentary on *The Secret of the Golden Flower* writing on the same theme speaks of "this being's lease" as the veil of *Maya* and the dominion of *Cupiditas.*

> The veil of *Maya* cannot be lifted by a mere decision of reason, but demands the most thoroughgoing and wearisome preparation consisting in the right payments of all debts to life. For so long as one is in any way held by the dominion of *cupiditas,* the veil is not lifted, and the heights of consciousness, empty of content and free of illusion, are not reached. . . . It is an ideal that can only be completely realised in death.

It is doubtful whether Keats had such "a thoroughgoing and wearisome preparation", but his poet's intuition went in a flashing mood of perception to "The Germinal Vesicle", "The Heavenly Heart" where Life and Consciousness are at one in the mysterious region of Death. In death it may be possible to achieve Life's high meed. Yet in the ordinary process of living the moments are rare when men can meet this vision.

It is possible to get glimpses of what this may mean, and no doubt Walt Whitman had similar intuitions about death, which he never tired of expressing in his poems. Many other writers have also touched this region of death, and have found a kind of sanctification; yet in the normal life of the soul the balance sways between Life and Consciousness, between the life-impulse to expand, to touch, to have, to know, (but which cannot know itself) and the impulse of consciousness that prunes the vine of life, that it may fruit, and more abundantly.

EPILOGUE

The preceding chapters propose a challenge to the Darwinian theory of evolution. This theory, and the attitude of mind that it fosters, is in close association with Marxian dialectic Materialism, in that each, in their own sphere, subordinate human nature to the workings of a scientific principle, which, by its nature, is abstract and exclusively rational. If at all successful in its enterprise, this book presents an alternative interpretation of biological facts, not unheedful of the development of genetics and embryology since Darwin's time. They present patterns of behaviour and growth that no easy rational explanation can possibly account for, and they put forward the idea that in the *background of the unknown* must be sought the solution of the problems they pose. The assumption is made that there exists, independent of our subjective thinking and feeling that so readily fabricates fantasies, *an objective and all-enfolding* reality which, existing in what may be thought of as a spiritual, disincarnate universe of thought, is finding incarnation in this world that we perceive with our senses.

The idea is as old, and older than the Gospels; the approach however is different, in that the discoveries of modern science are accepted. Yet rich as these are in scope and diversity, their development in the modern world is still held within a framework of enlightened rationalism that confines them in a state of psychic paralysis: – seeing they cannot see, and hearing they cannot hear."

At Cambridge when working as a student of Zoology I was affected by the prevailing paralysis, for it was only too easy to accept the Darwinian theory as the best possible working hypothesis. As a theory it coordinated a great number of facts. That it was, indeed, an *abstract* theory I hardly noticed at the time, nor did I perceive that the structure of learning built upon it prevented me from coming near to the understanding of my own human nature in my study of plant and animal life. Of my own nature and my relation to the world of living things I knew singularly little, and I accepted, with but small remonstrance, the implicit restraint set on the minds of contemporary biology students. I did not recognise that for enlightened rationalists a scientific theory that seemed to simplify the approach to the mystery of life is a very good means of defence against discovering what life and living are really like; and this because of the tremendous faith modern men have in anything that bears the label "scientific". This I might have perceived had there been time for speculation. All my days were given to learning a great number of facts, and these in themselves supplied interest enough. The principles of classification filled my mind to the exclusion of the all-important reality that nothing was done to help students of biology to an imaginative perception of living things. Only slowly in after years did such perception come to me. While living with two companions in the wilds of the North Australian bush, I began in that strange and illuminating atmosphere of solitude and close contact with the impulses of nature, to be aware of what lay behind, of what might lie behind the world of *wonder* that my senses presented to me. Coincident with my growing perceptions of life in nature, I became vaguely aware of some correspondence within myself which called for further discovery. Again, far later, after many years, I began the study of analytical psychology, seeking the unknown archetypes within the totality of my apprehension, and so coming back to the creatures that, in the words of the Oxyrhynchus Papyrus, are to draw us to the Kingdom.

> Ye ask who are these that draw us to the kingdom, if the Kingdom is in heaven? . . . the fowls of the air, and the beasts that are under the earth or upon the earth, and the

fishes of the sea, these are they that draw you; . . . And the Kingdom of Heaven is within you, and he who knows himself shall find it. Seek therefore to know yourselves and you will know that ye are the sons of the Father, and that ye are in the City of God, and that ye are the City.

APPENDIX I

THE PERIPHERAL FORCES OF NATURE

by the late George Adams

. . . In the seventeenth to nineteenth centuries, while physicists and astronomers were busily applying to their problems the ancient geometry of Euclid – rendered more handy and more elegant but in no way altered by the new analytical methods of Descartes, Leibniz and Newton – among pure mathematicians a new form of geometry was arising. It is a form which while including the Euclidean among other aspects is far more comprehensive, also more beautiful and more profound. I refer to the school of geometry variously known as Projective Geometry, modern Synthetic Geometry, or the Geometry of Position. In the seventeenth century its truths began to be apprehended by the astronomer Kepler and the mystical philosopher Pascal, also by Pascal's teacher, Girard Desargues, a less known but historically important figure. It was, however, in the early nineteenth century . . . that the new geometry really began to blossom forth. Once again, French mathematicians – among them Poncelet, Gergonne and Michel Chasles – were the pioneers, soon to be followed by a few brilliant thinkers in Switzerland and Germany, England, Italy and other countries. Largely unnoticed save among pure mathematicians, upon whose thought it was to have a deep and lasting influence, it grew into an even wider insight, which by the end of the century was seen to embrace most if not all of the known forms of geometry, Euclidean and non-Euclidean alike. Today . . . it opens out new ways of understanding Nature. . . .

Like that of Euclid, Projective Geometry is not only a discipline of pure thought, resting securely on its own ideal premises or axioms; it is also related to practical experience, though to begin with in a rather different direction. Our experience of the spatial world is above all visual and tactile. There are indeed other and less conscious senses – senses more "proprioceptive" of our own spatial body both in itself and in its interaction with the world, such as the sense of movement and that of balance – to which our spatial awareness and geometrical faculty are largely due. But in our outward consciousness it is the sense of touch and that of sight which reinforce and confirm geometrical reasoning and imagination. Now the geometry of Euclid relates above all to the sense of touch; hence too its natural connection with a scientific outlook taking its start from tangible material things. The inch, the foot, the yard, derive from our own body. We measure as we touch the earth, foot by foot and step by step, or in the rhythmic act of measurement with finger-tip and yardstick. By tactile experiences we confirm the constant distance between parallels, the symmetry laws of the right angle. We even prove the first theorem of Euclid by the imagined tactile experiment of applying one triangle to another. But our experience of space is also visual, and as such far more extensive, more manifold and satisfying. We see things we can never touch by hand or foot or tool; our vision reaches to the infinite horizon and to the stars. Now in the fifteenth to seventeenth centuries the beginnings of modern science coincided with the increasingly naturalistic art of the Renaissance. Both were inspired by the same love of Nature and wish to penetrate her secrets. So as to give an outwardly "true" picture of the scenes of landscape and the forms and works of men, artists such as Leonardo da Vinci and Durer studied the science of perspective vision, which from its practical and aesthetic applications presently gave birth to a new purely geometrical discipline – to wit, Projective Geometry. The latter, therefore, naturally deals not only with tangible and finite forms but with the *infinite* distance of space, represented as these are by the vanishing lines and vanishing points of perspective. Thus in the new geometry the infinitely distant is treated realistically, in a way that was foreign to the classical geometry of Euclid and the Greeks.

To include the infinitely distant, sometimes referred to as the "ideal elements" of space, no less definitely than those at a finite distance, is a bold step in thought, and is rewarded by a two-fold insight, of an importance hitherto unsuspected for the science of living things. (1) Attention is focused no longer on rigid forms such as the square or the circle, but on mobile *types of form,* changing into one another in the diverse aspects of perspective, or other kinds of geometrical transformation. In Euclid, for instance, we take our start from the rigid form of the circle, sharply distinguished from the ellipse, parabola and hyperbola, as are these from one another. In Projective Geometry it is the "conic section" in general of which the pure idea arises in the mind and of which various constructions are envisaged. As in real life the circular opening of a lamp-shade will appear in many forms of ellipse while moving about the room, or as the opening of a bicycle lamp projects on to the road in sundry hyperbolic forms, so in pure thought we follow the transformations from one form of conic section to another. Strictly speaking, the "conic section" of Projective Geometry is neither circle, ellipse, parabola nor hyperbola; it is a purely ideal form, out of which all of these arise, much as in Goethe's botany* the "archetypal leaf" is not identical with any particular variety or metamorphosis of leaf (foliage leaf varying in shape from node to node, petal, carpel and so on) but underlies them all.

The new geometry begets a quality of spatial thinking akin to the metamorphoses of living form. . . .

Projective Geometry recognizes as the deepest law of spatial structure an underlying *polarity* which to begin with may be

* *Goethe's Botanical Writings,* tr. by Bertha Mueller, Honolulu, 1952 R. Steiner, *Goethe the Scientist,* New York 1950. A. Arber, *The Natural Philosophy of Plant Form,* Cambridge, 1950.

called, in simple and imaginative language, a polarity of expansion and contraction, the terms being meant in a qualitative and very mobile sense. (If I now illustrate by using, after all, some of the more rigid and symmetrical forms, the limitations of which I have just referred to, it is only to make it easier by starting with familiar pictures.) Think of a sphere – not the internal volume but the pure form of the surface. One sphere can only differ from another as to size; apart from that, the form is the same. Now the expansion and contraction of a sphere leads too two ultimate limits. Contracted to the uttermost, the sphere turns into a point; expanded, into a plane. The latter transformation though calling for more careful reflection, is no less necessary than the former. A large spherical surface is less intensely curved than a small one; in other words, it is flatter. So long as it can still grow flatter, a sphere has yet not been expanded to the utmost limit, which can only be the absolute flatness of a plane . . . and . . . to be . . . space – that is, the space of our Universe and of our human imagination. Speaking qualitatively, the point is the quintessence of contraction, the plane of expansion. Here comes the fundamental difference as against both the old geometry of Euclid and the naive and rather earthly spatial notions which culminate in a one-sidely atomistic outlook. For in the light of the new geometry, three-dimensional space can equally well be formed from the plane inward as from the point outward. The one approach is no more basic than the other. In the old-fashioned explanation, we start from the point as the entity of no dimension. Moving the point, say from left to right, we obtain the straight line as the first dimension; moving the line forward and backward, we get the two dimensions of the plane; finally, moving the plane upward and downward, the full three dimensions. . . . In the . . . complementary aspect we should start from the plane and work inward. To mention only the first step: just as the movement of a point into a second point evokes the straight line that joins the two, so does the movement of a plane into a second plane give rise to the straight line in which the two planes interpenetrate. We can continue moving in the same line and obtain a whole sheaf of planes, like the leaves of an open book or a door swinging on its hinges. We thus obtain a "line of planes", as in the former instance a "line of points". In the space-creating polarity of point and plane, the straight line plays an intermediate role, equally balanced in either direction.

Just as two points of space always determine the unique straight line which joins them, so do two planes; we only need to recognize that parallel planes too have a straight line in common, namely the infinitely distant line of either. At last we see that all the intuitively given relationships of points, lines and planes have this dual or polar aspect. *Whatever is true of planes in relation to lines and points, is equally true of points in relation to lines and planes.* Three points, for example, not in line, determine a single plane (principle of the tripod), but so do three planes, not in line (e.g. the ceiling and two adjoining walls of a room) determine a single point. The planes must again be extended to the infinite and thought of as a whole to see that this is true without exception.

All spatial forms are ultimately made of points and planes. Even a plastic surface or a curve in space consists of an infinite and continuous sequence, not only of points, but of tangent lines and tangent or osculating planes. The mutual balance of these aspects – pointwise and planar, with the linewise aspect intermediating – gives us a deeper insight into the essence of plasticity than the old fashioned, one-sidedly pointwise treatment.

The outcome is whatever geometrical form or law we may conceive, there will always be a sister form, a sister law equally valid, in which the roles of point and plane are interchanged. Or else the form we thought of – as for example a tetrahedron with its equal number of points and planes – proves to be its own sister form, arising ideally out of itself by the polar interchange of point and plane. The principle just enunciated, as it were a master key among the truths of Projective Geometry, is known as the "Principle of Duality". It would perhaps have been better had it been described as a "Principle of Polarity" from the outset, for in its cosmic aspect it is also one of the essential keys to the manifold polarities of Nature. The recognition of it leads to a form of scientific thinking calculated to transcend one-sided atomism and materialistic bias.

A simple instance is shown in Figure 1. A sphere is placed inside a cube just large enough to contain it. Touching the six planes of the cube, the sphere picks out six points of contact. Joined three by three, the latter give eight planes, forming the double pyramid of the octahedron. Octahedron and cube are sister forms, in polar relation to one another. The structure and number relations are the same, only with plane and point – the principles of expansion and contraction – interchanged. The octahedron has *eight planes*, each of them bearing a triangle or triad of *points* and of the lines that join them; so has the cube *eight points*, each of them bearing a triad of *planes* and lines. The octahedron on the other hand has *six points* or apices, each with a four-fold structure, answering to the cube with its six four-square *planes*. The number of straight lines or edges in the same in each, namely twelve.

The sphere is only one of many spatial forms which evoke the polarity of plane and point – qualitatively speaking, of expansion and contraction. It does so only by actual contact as in Figure 1. For any given plane in space, the presence of a sphere evokes a point; for any given point, a plane. . . . The mutual relation is literally one of expansion and contraction, as shown in Figure 2. Here, on the left, we see the positions of cube and octahedron reversed as compared with Figure 1. The sphere is just large enough to fit inside the octahedron, touching the eight planes at the mid-points of the triangular faces. The points of contact obviously mark the eight corner-points of a cube, which is now inside the sphere. In the middle and right-hand pictures the size of the sphere is left unaltered, while in imagination we have deliberately caused the cube to contract towards the centre. The sphere preserves the mutual relation of cube and octahedron, only the octahedron now has to expand. For in the same proportion as the eight points of the cube recede, inwards from the surface of the sphere toward the centre, the corresponding planes hover outward causing the octahedron to expand even as the cube contracts. In the right-hand picture the cube is in linear dimensions half, the octahedron twice as big as on the left.

We can imagine the same process continued " to the bitter end ". The octahedron quickly grows, outward into the spatial universe. For when the cube is a hundred times smaller, the octahedron will be a hundred times bigger than before. And when at last the cube disappears, its eight corner-points merging into the single centre, we must imagine the eight planes of the octahedron coalescing in a single plane – the infinite periphery of space. . . . We thus arrive at another of the basic concepts of the new geometry, namely the single infinitely distant plane qua infinite periphery of space. It is the presence of this unique plane which from the indeterminate and ever mobile forms of pure Projective Space helps to produce the more rigidly determined space of the physical world, in other words the space of Euclid. We need only think of parallelism. Parallel lines and planes are those that meet at an infinite distance. Now as the crystals in Nature and human works of architecture show, parallelism plays an essential part in all the laws and measures of the physically spatial world. To the laws of parallelism must be added those of the right angle and of angular measure generally. These, too, are determined from the infinite periphery inward. The way in which this happens would take too long to explain in the present context, but the fact is evident, for we bear witness to it in every act of mensuration, when we take our sightings from the most distant points available – to be exact, from infinitely distant points.

Now my contention is that these ideas – the fundamentally planar and not only pointwise structure of universal space, and the mutually balanced relation of contractive and expansive, or centric and peripheral qualities, known to pure mathematicians, for well over a hundred years – should at long last be taken seriously in our understanding of real Nature. The same thing was suggested a few years ago by Professor H. W. Turnbull,* editor of Newton's correspondence now in course of publication. "In the realm of growth and form," write Professor Turnbull, referring to the pointwise and planewise aspects, "both analyses are significant. The seed, the stem and the leaf of a plant suggest two ways of studying the three dimensional shape, the one point-wise microscopically and the other planewise." He also draws attention to the fact that the relative completedness of a pointwise analysis, reached a certain scientific stage, neither excludes nor is vitiated by the polar opposite aspect which may still be awaiting discovery. "This mathematical duality is not a case of competing theories, where one is right and the other is wrong. . . . The characteristic description of their relationship is that of in and through but not of for or against." It is only a deeper and fuller insight which we may expect along these lines. Surely it is not unreasonable to suppose that Nature is built on the same principles which light up in the mind of man when he exercises one of the noblest of human faculties – that of clear geometric thinking and imagination

Let us now turn from the world of pure form to that of active forces. Here once again, since Newton, Faraday and Clerk Maxwell, clear geometrical and mathematical thinking has enabled us to master the play of physical forces, such as the force of gravitation, the momentum of heavy bodies, the electric and magnetic forces. Primarily, we know of these not by

* H. W. Turnbull, "Mathematics in the Larger Context". *Research* Vol. 3, no. 5, 1950.

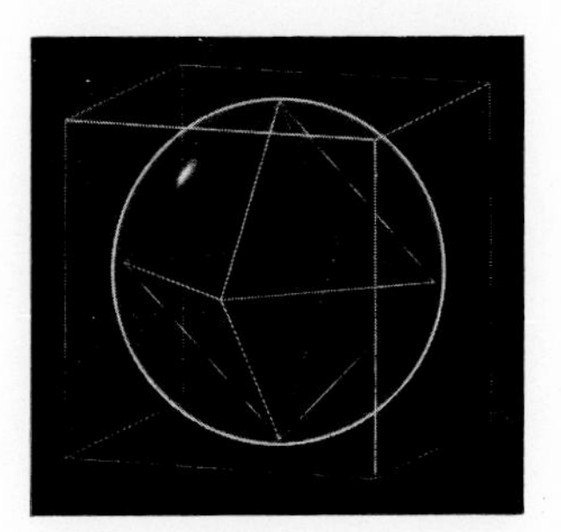

Fig. 1

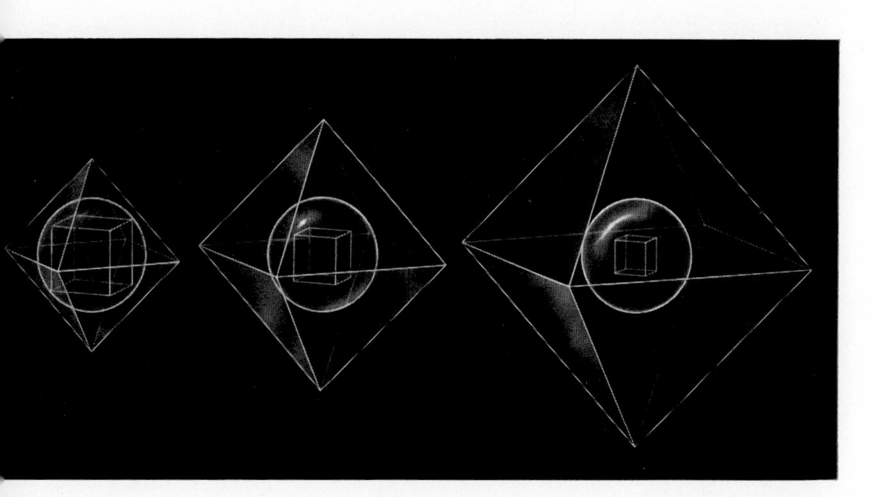

Fig. 2

dint of thought alone, but by experiment and observation. Unlike that of velocities or of accelerations (though some of the text-books fail to make this clear), the "parallelogram of forces" cannot be proved by any reasoning or definition; it is a fact of experience, confirmed as accurately as we like by many kinds of experiment. But though we only know of them empirically to begin with, Nature reveals that in their interplay and balance the physical forces obey mathematical laws. When we discover these laws and bring our minds into harmony with them, we learn to understand and master the play of forces. Hence all the power of our applied science and technology. Now it is characteristic of nearly all the forces known to physics that they are point-centred. These are the kind of forces which emanate from heavy matter; it is only natural that we have found them first, since physical science took its start from mechanics – from the investigation of the cruder properties of matter. But this was also due to the prevailing forms of thought. Man naturally notices what he is wont to think, and things escape his notice even if he sees them, if the idea that is in them is foreign to his mind. Through his Euclidean schooling, the spatial thinking of the scientist has hitherto been one-sided centric and pointwise. He has the mental equipment for understanding centric forces; no wonder he finds them.

For sake of brevity may I now put as a categorical statement what I certainly do not intend thus dogmatically, for like any other scientific proposition, it is only stated to be put to the test. *The forces of Nature, manifesting in the world of space and time, are not only centric; there are peripheral forces also.* Even as the pure form of space is in the light of modern geometry balanced between point and plane, so are the forces that prevail in Nature; they are not only pointwise or centric but peripheral or planar. Moreover, as in the domain of centric forces the central point of the material planet on which we live, in other words the centre of gravity of the earth, is for us a centre of primary importance, so in the realm of the peripheral or planar forces, what we experience as the infinitely distant plane—in simple language the vast periphery of the blue sky—is a most important source of the peripheral forces.

This, I shall now endeavour to explain, is an ideal key to what you are really doing when you enhance the power of your medicaments by the rhythmic process of expansion or dilution. But let me first point out that the idea of peripheral forces is not altogether new. Under the name of "ethereal forces" or by other kindred forms of description they have been known since time immemorial. In the East, their reality has never ceased to be recognised. They only need to be rediscovered in terms of modern science. In the seventeenth century a more or less instinctive knowledge of them still lingered on traditionally, but had grown so confused that the new science, based on experiment and reason, could make nothing of it. Tradition undoubtedly helped give rise to Huyghens' idea of a "luminiferous ether", but this too was interpreted in terms of physical and centric forces and was to that extent a misunderstanding, which has in any case been abandoned by twentieth-century physics. The new geometry on the other hand, grown to maturity during the nineteenth century, gives us the possibility of understanding the ethereal qua peripheral forces in a strictly scientific sense. They are forces related above all to the realm of life, just as the centric forces—gravitational, electro-magnetic and so on—manifest most strongly in the sphere of inorganic matter. By sensitive and spiritually developed people, though often called by different names or not named at all, they can be known from direct experience.

The late Rudolf Steiner* to whom I am most indebted in this connection, was always at pains to integrate with scientific

* R. Steiner and I. Wegman, *Fundamentals of Therapy*, London, 1925, ch. III. See also the lecture by R. Steiner, 9th April, 1922, in *The Golden Blade*, 1961.

method what is experienced by subtler and more spiritual modes of cognition. . . . He distinguishes between the forces – manifested above all in the lifeless realm – emanating from material centres, and another kind of force, working not outward from any earthly centre but inward from the periphery, generally from the surrounding Cosmos. In spatial character he describes them succinctly as "forces which have not a centre but a periphery". They tend indeed towards the material bodies of living things – above all towards the germinating centres of fresh life – *but the relative centre towards which they work is not their source, rather than their infinite** receiver. We must invert the accustomed functional notions of centre and periphery to get the right idea. A physical force emanating from a centre needs the surrounding space into which to ray out. The infinite periphery has to be there to receive it. So does an ethereal or peripheral force need the living centre towards which it works. It springs from the periphery, from the vast expanse, and tends towards the living centre which it endows, just as the physical force springs from a centre, from a place of concentration, and works outward.† In lectures to scientists towards the end of his life, Steiner himself referred to Projective Geometry as a valuable pathway along which such ideas could be elaborated.

The ethereal or peripheral forces, in the nature of the case, have more to do with living growth and development, with the "becoming" of things. If there were only rigid and finished forms the old Euclidean geometry might suffice us. To understand the genesis and metamorphosis of living forms we need a more mobile thinking, and one that reveals the balance

* My italics. E. L. G. W.

† G. Adams and O. Whicher, *The Living Plant and the Science of Physical and Ethereal Spaces*, 1949; *The Plant between Sun and Earth*, 1952 (Goethean Science Foundation, Clent, Worcs.); *Die Pflanze in Raum und Gegenraum*, Stuttgart, 1960. G. Adams, "Universalkräfte in der Mechanik", in *Mathematisch-Physikalische Korrespondenz*, ed. by Dr. G. Unger, Dornach, Switzerland, 1956-59.

L. Locher-Ernst, *Raum und Gegenraum*, Dornach, 1957.

between the centric and peripheral, architectural and plastic aspects. Yet even the most rigid of Nature's forms, that of the crystal, is understood in a far deeper way (as any crystallographer with an elementary knowledge of Projective Geometry may confirm) when we perceive how the crystal lattice derives from an archetypal pattern in the infinitely distant plane – the infinite periphery of universal space.* In the realm of living form, once the new geometrical idea has been awakened in the mind, morphology and embryology confirm what is known to us by simple everyday experience from the world of plants – how life on earth is sustained by forces flowing inward from the surrounding heavens. Biology has hitherto been trying to understand these things with concepts derived from the inorganic world, where centric forces predominate. As has been said by Bertalanffy among others, it has in some ways been a hindrance to biological thinking to have to borrow its basic concepts from the non-biological sciences of physics and physical chemistry. Ideas no less scientifically exact should be derivable directly from the study of living phenomena even as the ideas of mechanics and electromagnetics have been derived from the study of non-living things. Far from implying a gulf between the living and the non-living, it would then be found that the ideas derived from the world of life reveal the non-living too in a deeper aspect. . . .

From a lecture given to The British Homoeopathic Congress, London, 1 June, 1961.

* See the Author's *Space and the Light of the Creation*, London, 1933; *Strahlende Weltgestaltung*, Dornach, 1934.

APPENDIX II

NOTE ON THE MAYFLY

This transformation from green-drake to grey-drake is cited because it demonstrates a transformation of an imago into a further development. The change from a creature which appears as mature into a yet further stage. The mayfly *Ephemera vulgata,* a fly with four pearly lacelike wings and three long hairs on the tail appears in numbers in May and June. They love to dance in their scores and hundreds together, whizzing vertically upwards for a few feet, then letting themselves float downwards, then rising again. They may be seen as things so aetherealised as not to need to eat. They have no effective gullet or mouth-parts; they live but for a few hours to dance in the sun, breed and die. They emerge from a larval form that has lived in the underwater mud of rivers. At the appointed time they rise quickly to the surface, and then with astonishing quickness change into the Green Drake form. In this state they are capable of flying, and appear as complete and mature insects. In a short while, however, they have a second change, and the Grey Drake emerges from the Green Drake. These may be considered as the mature insects, as this is the form that lays the eggs. This second change might seem unnecessary, but so it is. And so it may be that a second change is demanded in the psychic development in men.

INDEX

Printed in Great Britain by Northumberland Press Ltd, Gateshead on Tyne